NEW LEAF PAPER®

E N V I R O N M E N T A L B E N E F I T S S T A T E M E N T

of using post-consumer waste fiber vs. virgin fiber

Rocket Mass Heaters saved the following resources by using New Leaf EcoBook 50, made with 100% recycled fiber, 50% post-consumer waste, and processed chlorine free.

trees	water	energy	solid waste	greenhouse gases
5	**1,622**	**3**	**212**	**363**
fully grown	gallons	million Btu	pounds	pounds

Calculations based on research by Environmental Defense and other members of the Paper Task Force.

©2007 New Leaf Paper   www.newleafpaper.com

ROCKET MASS HEATERS:

Superefficient Woodstoves YOU Can Build

The New Updated Version of:

Rocket Stoves to Heat Cob Buildings

Ianto Evans
Leslie Jackson

A Cob Cottage Company Publication
2006, 2007

This book is obtainable by mail order from
Cob Cottage Company
Box 942
Coquille, OR 97423
Phone (541) 396-1825
Website: www.cobcottage.com
$22 cash (includes shipping) or USPS money order
($35 for two). Cheques, add $5.
Bulk orders: Ten for $99. Orders of eleven or more, $9 each.

This book is also obtainable in .pdf format from www.rocketstoves.com

First Edition Notes: This is a long-overdue book on a unique heating system that will be invaluable and fascinating to any people who want to heat with wood and be comfortable 24 hours a day. Only a handful of people have been pyromaniacal and hardy enough to try to build Rocket Mass Heaters charged by a Rocked Stove. *You are now joining that handful.*

Following further research and feedback from readers, an expanded edition is planned. If you make a substantial contribution to the new edition, we'll send you two copies when it is published. –August, 2004

Second Edition Notes: Here, since its first printing in 2004, is published the updated story of the Rocket Mass Heater for cob buildings, with theories and detailed descriptions of how we and people we know have built successful models. It includes improved and expanded drawings. Since its first printing, many of our friends have designed and built their own Rocket Stoves, using this book as their diving board. They appear in this edition with the results of their inventions, experiments and discoveries. We invite and encourage you to test these methods for yourself and use your pyro-wisdom and creativity to come up with your own version, with the caution that this science is speculative because there has been little development of it until now.

All illustrations are copyright Ianto Evans or Leslie Jackson, unless otherwise noted. The text is non-copyright. You are welcome to use it in any way you want, but please acknowledge your source. We just want people to get stoveing and stop supporting the utility corporations. It does help our work if you buy books directly from Cob Cottage Co. or Leslie Jackson. Buy a dozen or a whole case, give them as presents or sell them at gatherings, classes, conferences, etc. It will pay for your firewood. –February, 2006

ROCKET MASS HEATERS

Table of Contents

What this Book is About

This little book is about a revolutionary concept in wood burning stoves that ensures almost completely clean combustion with high efficiency use of the heat produced. Rocket Stoves are still experimental in that only a few hundred were in regular use by early 2006, but some have performed well, daily, for more than a decade. They save a lot of fuel and completely rearrange our concepts of house heating, of wood burning, and of dependency on coal, oil, hydro- or nuclear power for our comfort. Rocket Mass Stoves can be built at home by relatively unskilled people. While they are well-suited to earthen buildings with their thermally massive walls, floors and built-in furniture, they can be built into any kind of structure—from cargo containers to yurts.

The term Rocket Stove has been used loosely for about twenty years to mean a fairly wide range of combustion devices used for cooking and heating.

Aside from the model described in detail in this book, Rocket principles have been variously applied. Larry Jacobs and I came up with a version using only a metal drum and two stovepipes, later called the Pocket Rocket (see Detroitus: The Pocket Rocket). Later, in the late 1980's, I helped develop a lightweight concrete single pot cook stove for urban Guatemalans. More recently, small portable cook stoves have been developed using tin cans and simple insulation. Experimental rocket-fired ovens and water heaters have also been built.

Perhaps most significantly, the Rocket Mass Stoves used for house heating, which are now starting to appear all over North America and Northern Europe, have real promise in that they improve comfort and reduce the amount of fuel burned, thereby lessening the load of CO_2 on greenhouse gases. They turn almost all the wood into heat, and can store almost all of the heat generated for optimal comfort when you need it.

Who this Book is For

This manual is intended for pyromaniacs, tinkerers, people with curiosity about fire, owner-builders, people with an experimental mind, do-it-yourself builders who want to be less dependent on the system and have environmental concerns, and above all, those who want to be snug at home. The realm of Rocket Stoves is an experimental one whose time is overdue. Play and innovation are highly recommended. As our friend Tom Frame (see Case Studies, page 80) says, "Don't be afraid to try something new or different. Don't have the right part? Try something else. Can't make a quick phone call for answers? Trust your own judgment. Just can't figure it out? Wait, be patient. Move on to something else if you can. The answer will come. Most importantly, don't rush this thing! You really want it to work when you're done building it. Take the time needed."

The model of heating Rocket we describe suits the Maritime Pacific climate quite well, but it is not limited to it. Once you understand the principles of the Rocket Mass Stove, you'll be able to modify it to your own heating needs.

Rocket Stoves' design is exploratory; their use is experimental; the attention they demand may keep you in fascination or you may find their quirks irritating. For the next edition, we will look forward to hearing (and learning from) your feedback, comments, stumbling blocks, epiphanies and wild fancies. So fire away, so to speak; send us images and drawings. If we use your material, we'll send you two copies of the new edition.

THE FINE PRINT

Neither Ianto Evans, Leslie Jackson, nor Cob Cottage Company can be held in any way responsible for damage, fire or injury arising from the use of this material. These stoves are experimental and, besides, we don't have any assets. So, enjoy to the full your fire damage and injuries. For some precautions, see Fire! Fire! (page 58).

The Combustion Unit...

The Rocket Stove in Ianto Evans's cottage, seen from above. Dry firewood, cut thin, the small feed barrel with lid and the large heat riser barrel with tea kettle.

...is connected to the Thermal Battery

Ianto demonstrates the stove's use.

Cross-Section of a Typical Rocket Mass Heater

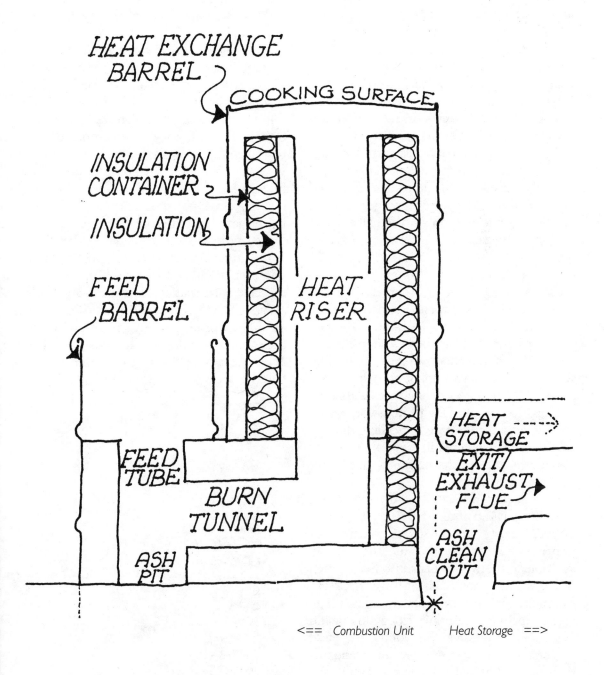

HEAT EXCHANGE BARREL

COOKING SURFACE

INSULATION CONTAINER

INSULATION

FEED BARREL

HEAT RISER

FEED TUBE

BURN TUNNEL

HEAT STORAGE

EXIT/ EXHAUST FLUE

ASH PIT

ASH CLEAN OUT

<== Combustion Unit   Heat Storage ==>

Ianto Knows Why Rocket Stoves

Rocket Stoves grew out of work I did between 1976 and the late 1980's, mostly on solutions to the international firewood crisis and the problem of smoke in the homes of traditional people. In Guatemala in the 70's, I helped worked on the Lorena stove system, which uses a sand-clay amalgam to contain the fire, hold up the pots and store surplus heat. It rapidly attracted worldwide attention and is now widely used in Latin America, Asia and Africa. Later, I worked as part of a team in over twenty countries, helping people create better cooking facilities. I spent much of a decade in villages, in people's homes, mostly with the women who actually do the cooking. One result of my experience as a professional pyromaniac was some work in the US on the challenge of improving wood-fired heating stoves for cold climates.

At that time, wood stoves had scarcely improved in more than a hundred years. The basic format had always been a simple metal box with an attached exhaust pipe. The stove heats the surrounding air, which rises to heat the ceiling, gradually circulating as it cools. To be optimally heated, you would need to be staked out on the ceiling directly over the stove. In general, the more heat lost out of the top of the chimney, the better the combustion.

Clearly, this in itself is wildly inefficient. The sky has no interest in being heated. Worse, most wood stoves burn very imperfectly, that is, not all the energy available in the wood turns into heat. Much of the wood's potential heat leaves the stove as smoke, particles, and unburned gases. The results include poisoning your downwind neighbors, excessive firewood use, and personal frustration. Clean air standards imposed by the federal government in the 1980's attempted to limit the amount of smoke and particles put out by commercial wood stoves, but came nowhere close to ensuring clean burning.

Our goal in developing Rocket type stoves was to rethink completely the question of how to burn wood inside a house in order to improve human comfort, use less firewood, and cut pollution.

The results are impressive. In my own cottage I burn only about two-thirds of a cord of (fir and alder) firewood a year, while my neighbors average 3–5 cords. You can usually tell when any of the neighbors are around by the cloud of smoke coming out of their chimneys. By contrast, we burn so clean that visitors coming into my house want to know how come it's so snug without the stove burning. Imagine their surprise when they learn that in fact, it is burning merrily.

As I write, I sit by my own Rocket Stove, in my little cob house in the depth of Oregon winter. I built this stove myself in a day from recycled parts that cost less than $50.

Since the late 1980's, Rocket Mass Stoves have been my only heat source apart from the sun. For seventeen years I have daily been able to evaluate these heaters that suit me better than anything else I can find.

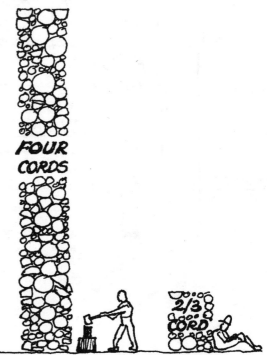

A comparison of a year's supply of wood. The left stack is my neighbor's, the right is mine.

Significant Features of Rocket Heating Stoves

1. A roughly J-shaped combustion chamber with abrupt right angle turns. Hot gases rising up the long leg suck cool air down the short leg through the fuel.

2. A combustion chamber enclosed in high temperature insulation. (Insulation = high temperature = complete combustion = high efficiency).

3. An insulated chimney which is inside the stove itself (creates draft).

4. The firewood stands upright and burns at its bottom end only, feeding the stove by gravity as it falls into the fire.

5. The capacity to push heated gases through long horizontal passages in floors, beds, or benches.

6. The concept of separating the combustion unit from the use of the heat so produced, and particularly, storing that heat for hours or days in inexpensive built-in furniture.

7. Extraordinary efficiency, both in extracting heat from the fuel and in delivering heat for use when and where it is needed.

8. Easy to construct from inexpensive materials.

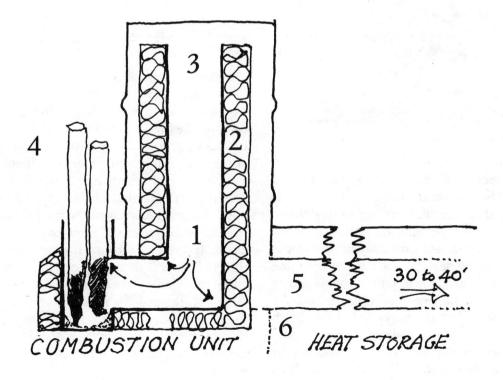

COMBUSTION UNIT   HEAT STORAGE

Draft Works the Stove

Campfires

A campfire burns wood in the open air, outdoors. Its combustion success depends upon a steady flow of air. Oxygen, which constitutes a fifth of our air, combines with volatile oils and other gaseous products boiled out of the wood, generating heat. You can't heat yourself by contact; the coals are too hot; you would get burned, and if you were to sit in the hot gases trying to warm up, you would be slowly smoked and then asphyxiate. For heating people, only direct radiation is available from the coals and flame. But most of the heat is normally wasted. You can only warm up at a distance beside the fire.

Try a simple experiment:
Hold any kind of cardboard or metal tube over a smoldering campfire, tight over the embers. The fire will immediately come to life, the embers will glow brighter and the smoke will lessen.
It will burn better.

Campfire: Heats mostly by radiation.

Chimneys

Chimneys suck. They draw air up themselves because the gas in them is hotter than the air that surrounds them. The draw is dependant on both the height and the average interior temperature: height multiplied by heat. So you can get the same effect from a very tall, rather cool chimney (as in most factories) or conversely, by a short, very hot chimney. A 100 foot high chimney that is twenty degrees warmer than the surrounding air generates roughly as much draw as a chimney just two feet high but a thousand degrees hotter.

Wood Stoves

A wood stove is a fireproof container with a fire inside it. For oxygen to be drawn through the fuel, a chimney carries hot gases up, sucking cold air in past the fuel (and perhaps through your house). Hopefully, sufficient air is drawn in, or the fuel will merely pyrolyze—that is bake out the volatile oils without burning them—producing smoke which lacks sufficient oxygen to be burnt. If there is too much air coming in, the cold air will dilute the hot gases in the chimney and lower the combustion temperature, making the burn worse. For the whole thing to work, the chimney must be hot, and if it is outside the building, valuable heat is lost from the building to the sky.

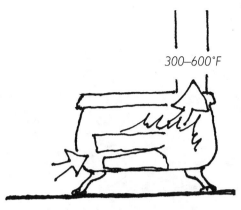

A metal box stove is an advance over an open fire, but still wastes a lot of heat.

With a shelf damper, the situation is better: A cleaner burn and a lower exit temperature.

Rocket Stoves are Different

The revolutionary part of Rocket heating stoves is the concept of **putting the chimney (the heat riser) inside the stove**. This is done by enclosing the heat riser so that exhaust gases are captured with almost all the heat still in them. Then, by running these gases through a masonry mass, they are encouraged to cool before leaving the building.

The stove inside my own home has an internal chimney about 3 feet high, which runs at between 1200 and 1800°F. The metal barrel that surrounds the chimney radiates enough heat that the combustion gases are down to perhaps 500–700°F by the time they leave the stove. But now instead of wasting that heat by discharging hot gas from my house, we feed it through a cob and rock day bed and seat so that it is down to between 90° and 200°F by the time it leaves the building.

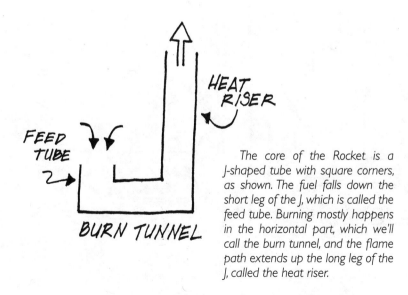

The core of the Rocket is a J-shaped tube with square corners, as shown. The fuel falls down the short leg of the J, which is called the feed tube. Burning mostly happens in the horizontal part, which we'll call the burn tunnel, and the flame path extends up the long leg of the J, called the heat riser.

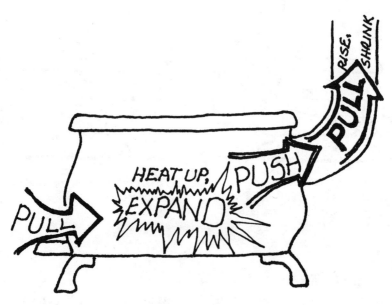

A metal box stove pushes hot gas up the stack, which in turn pulls air through the box.

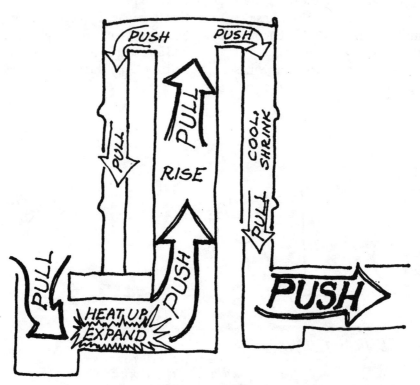

A Rocket Stove pushes hot gases through a thermal battery to heat your body by contact.

Combustion and Heat

HOW WOOD BURNS

The air we breathe is about 20% oxygen. Oxygen is super-reactive and will combine at the right temperature with almost anything and burn it, releasing energy as heat. Different materials catch fire at different temperatures. For instance phosphorous will burn just by exposure to oxygen at room temperature, but steel needs to be heated to thousands of degrees in order to burn. When wood is first heated, the lignin and cellulose, which comprise most of its bulk, break down into a big range of simple to complex chemical gases. When they reach a certain temperature, they ignite and burn, combining with oxygen and producing flames, in a process known as combustion.

Watch a piece of firewood throughout its burn cycle, from when heat is first applied all the way to ash. First (a), you'll notice steam and pale visible gases squirting out as they reach boiling point inside the wood. Then (b), there will be smoke, blue or grey or sometimes black, difficult to breathe, smelling toxic (it is). Gradually (c), the outer parts will begin to glow as (d), the smoke catches fire. Then finally just (e), glowing coals, no smoke, no big flames, just little blue ones as those coals burn.

You just watched (a) the wood heating up and drying out, (b) the volatile oils boiling out as cellulose and lignin pyrolize (break down under heat) into other chemicals, hundreds of them. When conditions are hot enough (c) the carbon which remains from pyrolysis, the charcoal, will then burn, glowing, creating carbon monoxide giving off heat and (d) the smoke catches fire with long yellow flames, turning itself into carbon dioxide and water vapor, and of course also giving off heat. Finally (e) the smoke is all gone, coals remain, glowing. Those short blue flames you see are the carbon monoxide burning, creating carbon dioxide and producing again more heat.

If there is insufficient oxygen, combustion will be incomplete, producing more smoke and carbon monoxide and, of course, less heat. The same happens if the burn zone is too cool or if oxygen is arriving too fast (blow out a candle). Campfires often smoke at first for lack of heat, but they also smoke if you restrict their air flow with wet leaves, shoveling dirt on, etc. The perfect stove has just enough oxygen, dispersed through the smoke gases, and a high enough temperature that everything burns down to only water vapor, carbon dioxide, *heat* and a little ash.

Given the problems of carbon dioxide and its notoriety as a greenhouse gas, people are sometimes shocked to hear that the stove puts it out, yet any wood stove even burning cleanly will put out carbon dioxide, as will a coal, oil or gas-burning power station, or a car using gasoline. The cleaner we burn wood, the less we use because we're burning more efficiently, thus creating less carbon dioxide. To be responsible, we need not to stop burning hydrocarbon fuels, but *to reduce* their use to a safe level. This is a good reason not just for clean burning wood stoves, but also for smaller houses, passive solar homes, snugger spaces, heating your body directly by contact, and not heating anything that you don't need to.

For a detailed readable further discussion see *The Woodburner's Encyclopedia* or *Heating Your Home with Wood* (see Recommended Books).

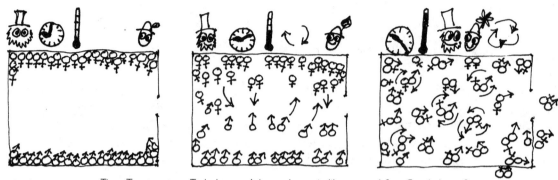

Time, Temperature, Turbulence. A barn dance is like a good fire. Good clean fun.

The Three T's

In seeking a clean burn, think 3-Ts: Time, Temperature, Turbulence. The molecules of oxygen and of the combustion gases all need to be able to find each other as well as commingle. It's like one of those huge country dances, where all the men line up on one wall, and all the women on the opposite one. When the music begins, everyone surges out onto the dance floor, looking for a partner of the opposite gender. For everyone to pair up, the tune needs to be prolonged (time), the music fast (temperature) and the dance rambunctious (there's your turbulence).

So your combustion unit needs an **insulated** combustion chamber (in order to maintain the dancers at a high temperature), a **tall** enough heat riser that all the oxygen is used up (as the hot, lightweight dancers strut and spin their way up it), and a non-streamlined profile to **tumble** the gases (shakin' their boogilators, as they say). Hence the **abrupt right-angle turns** in a Rocket Stove's interior.

The Thermal Battery

Even with the wood burning at a hundred percent efficiency, if we waste the heat by not using it, efficiency is moot. The cleanest burning conventional wood stove with a platinum afterburner may well burn all the wood cleanly, but in order to function at all, it needs to waste a proportion of the heat generated by discharging it up the exhaust pipe.

Unlike a conventional wood stove, Rocket Stoves don't need to waste heat to maintain a burn. The combustion unit at the core of a rocket stove turns wood into only carbon dioxide and water vapor with a little wood ash and heat. How we use that heat is a separate story.

Whereas with a wood stove, the chimney sucks cool air through the stove and pumps hot gases out of the building, the Rocket Stove creates pressure that we can guide and control in order to literally **direct the heat to wherever we need it.** We can cook with it or heat water or heat our houses or heat ourselves.

By attaching the Rocket Stove to a heat storage device, we are able to soak up the heat from the exhaust gases and store it for quite long periods. The 3-ton double bed attached to the rocket stove in our office stays noticeably warm for about three days after being heated up. It acts as a thermal battery, storing heat while the stove is burning, then releasing it slowly.

Note that in the heat storage—that is, the part downstream from the combustion unit—turbulence is not desirable. Any obstruction which would cause turbulence will affect the draw. On the other hand, exhaust gases move much slower than in a conventional wood stove so tight bends will be much less of a problem in a pipe of 6-inch or greater diameter. Long residency time and high temperature are both assets, at least near to the combustion unit.

HOW HEAT MOVES

Heat is forever redistributing itself, the warmer parts of the universe constantly attempting democracy by generously heating their cooler surrounds. Anything warmer will always try to heat something cooler. If the temperature difference is great, the heat flow is faster, though impediments to heat transfer (insulants) will always slow it down. Remember that heat as flowing from warmer to cooler by three separate modes: radiation, convection and conduction.

Radiation is the direct transfer of energy through space. Sometimes it comes in the form of visible light, for instance sunshine; often the wavelength is longer and therefore invisible to us as is the heat from a metal wood stove. Sometimes it's a mixture, as at a campfire, or when you look down into the toaster, (which is a totally radiant heater with both visible and invisible rays singeing your bread).

Radiation moves in straight lines, in every direction, up, down and all around simultaneously through space until it meets a solid, where it is reflected and absorbed in varying proportions. Some surfaces such as polished aluminum reflect a high percentage. Skin, on the other hand, absorbs a much larger share, happily if you're cold and rather unfortunately if you're too hot.

All of this is useful if you are building a campfire, which heats you only by radiation, or a toaster, which is a radiant cooker. As a way of being comfortable, however, radiation has drawbacks. An obvious one is that it heats only exposed surfaces. Your front can be overheated while your back is freezing and clothing may prevent a radiator from heating you at all. To radiate best, stove surfaces need to be at dangerously high temperatures, and as the radiant surface changes temperature with the complexity of wood burning, you have to keep moving to stay comfy.

The **amount** of radiation received is proportional to how hot the source is and how far away it is. A hotter radiant surface loses disproportionally more heat as it warms up. If you get twice as close to a hot stove, you still get more than twice the heat.

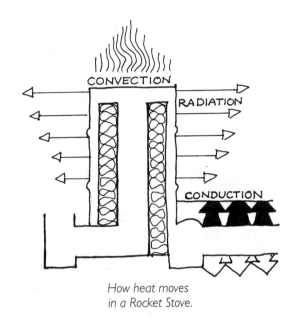

How heat moves in a Rocket Stove.

Convection is heat transfer by the bodily movement of a gas or a liquid. Smoke rises because it is warmer than the surrounding air. Peer into a glass of hot cocoa or miso soup and you will see a lot of movement as the warmer liquid rises and the cooler falls. It's all convection. A "convection oven" however, isn't—it has a fan. It is another misnomer that "radiators" under windows that heat public buildings are radiators because they really are convectors. They can't get hot enough to be effective as radiators as they would be too far away from most people. Most of the heat from those "radiators" is carried upward in moving air.

As a mode for heating people, convection isn't all that useful. To be warmed by convection, you need to be above the heat source. The best place to be comfortable for convective heating in a house is usually against the ceiling, where the warmest air ends up, and convective heating from a fireplace would have you located in the chimney, unless your fire smokes into the room.

***Conduction* is heating by contact.** When you shake hands with someone, if you think they have a cold hand it's because you're donating to them some of your body warmth. As with all heat transfer, conduction always flows from hotter to colder, however small the difference may be. If everything else is equal it flows equally in all directions, all around and up and down. "But doesn't heat always rise?" No, only by convection. Heat rising is not a characteristic of either radiation or conduction.

Conduction is most apparent through solids, depending upon how well the solid allows heat to pass through it. Conductivity varies a lot, from that of still air, which is extremely low, to that of metal (sit on an aluminum chair on a cold day).

Somewhere in between are masonry materials. The denser they are, the faster they transmit heat. Limestone and brick are medium-fast conductors; granite and basalt are faster; iron ore would be even faster because it's heavier. Denser materials and those that contain metal can be dangerously conductive, such as hot stones straight out of a campfire or a cast-iron frying pan's hot handle. They conduct faster because they're heavier.

In houses, conduction is rarely used for personal comfort. Fireplaces give us none at all, the warm parts are all far too hot to touch, and the same is true for most metal box stoves. We use hot water bottles, electric blankets and hot tea, all with quite brief effects. Cuddling with someone else is useful but not always practical. Most houses have only one conductive way to warm up fast; take a hot shower.

***Insulation* is any material that slows the passage of heat transfer.** To delay heat moving by conduction, a good rule of thumb is to choose the most lightweight material available. Lightweight usually means there is air trapped in it. A down parka, sheep's wool socks, or a fiber-filled bed quilt all contribute to our comfort by trapping air, one of the most effective insulants known.

At high temperatures, most biological insulants either burn or fall apart and foamboards melt and offgas dangerous toxins. For stove construction we need mineral insulants such as pumice, vermiculite or perlite. Clay is less insulating though not nearly as bad as sand, which is a lot heavier.

COMFORT THROUGH STORED HEAT

The Rocket Stove is a thermal pump that shoves out hot gas which can be used to heat built-in furniture. It can easily push hot gas through 30 or 40 feet of horizontal pipes, storing heat in the interior walls, floor or seating in a house. By sitting or lying on a heated seat, your body is warmed directly wherever it makes contact. You also bask in the warm air rising from that seat. In my own house I can comfortably do paperwork, sitting on the bench that my Rocket Stove heats when the temperature in the room is in the 50's. To be as comfy by heating all of the air in the building, the temperature would have to be in the 70's. Rocket Stoves take what would otherwise be wasted chimney heat to warm built-in furniture such as beds, couches and chairs, as well as floors and interior walls.

We live in surprising times. Every so often one can wake up to a societal myth that one has accepted all one's life. The myth that *houses need to be heated* permeates North America and society has encapsulated this obvious fable in law. Building regulations have demanded that whether you're home or not, every single corner of the interior of your house should be heatable to an equal 70°F. Let's be clear. Provided you don't let the water freeze, your house could not care less whether it's heated. The inhabitants are the only beings who count. We want to heat people, not houses. Once we understand this, the situation gets much easier.

Humans, like all mammals, are self-heating. We have our own internal stoves, burning food to make heat. But as we become less physically active and spend more time indoors, we have become used to wearing clothes to slow the loss of our autonomously generated heat. In an unheated building we can adjust our comfort by adding clothes or through activity or by surrounding ourselves with warmth or through all three.

Houses heated by forced air or furnaces depend upon our bodies being in contact only with the warmed air inside the house. A house can contain an awful lot of warm air, of which only a very small proportion ever comes in contact with us. All of the other heat is effectively wasted. Air, being one of the best insulants, certainly isn't a fast or efficient way to warm up, and it escapes easily.

Standard Box Stove

Rocket Stove

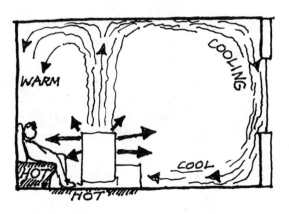

How Rocket Stove heat is different.

Step-by-Step Construction

For first-time builders, we will describe a single well-tested model that we know will work well and is easy to build. The stove in my own house is similar; the Cob Cottage Company's office has one almost identical, as has the North American School of Natural Building. Here is a suggested order for designing the stove and its attached heat storage, materials and tools needed, dimensions and proportions, actual construction of the combustion unit, and finally the heat storage unit.

1. In an existing building, examine the site where the stove will be built.
2. Measure the space available.
3. Design your stove and heat storage unit.
4. Do a scale drawing of brick layout.
5. Assemble tools and materials (see list, page 29).
6. Clean all bricks, burn paint off barrels, make sure all pipes fit together, straighten them if necessary.
7. Build a mock-up of the combustion chamber outdoors. Use the materials you will build the permanent stove with.
8. Build a test fire in the mock-up.
9. Experiment with the test model in order to trouble-shoot and optimize your system.
10. Mix mortar, then insulation, then cob.
11. Level and compact stove site, if needed.
12. Roughly draw out position of the base of the entire device, including ducts, etc. Adjust as necessary, *in situ.*
13. Re-check the design. Does it still make sense?
14. Install any insulation needed below the stove.
15. Build the combustion chamber including the heat riser, one full course of bricks at a time. Check level and plumb at each course.
16. Install the small barrel at the feed hole.
17. Set up containment for insulation around the heat riser.
18. Pack insulation in.
19. Install big barrel around the heat riser.
20. Now test combustion again. Adjust barrel position to give heat where you want it.
21. Connect all the parts of the internal duct work.
22. Open all the windows and test drive.
23. Build heat storage.
24. Test drive again.
25. Clean up.
26. Fire up stove, put on tea.
27. Heat up the house and invite all the neighbors to the feast.

Designing Your Stove and Thermal Battery

THE COMBUSTION UNIT

The combustion unit for a system that uses 8-inch diameter pipes, combustion chamber and flue will measure about 4 feet long by 3 feet high by 2 feet front-to-back, though it can take up less vertical space if you sink the whole thing into your floor. A six-inch diameter pipe system could be a little smaller.

For your first-time build, play it safe with an **established and tested model of the combustion unit.** The heat storage, on the other hand, can be custom designed to reflect your family's needs. Don't try a complete floor heater the first time around, but you have many options for heat storage in your snug corner, your heated bench or a warm bed.

In very cold areas and a house over 1200 square feet, you may need a bigger system altogether, including a larger barrel. There's probably a limit to how big you could build a Rocket without very specialized, high temperature materials. You don't want the whole thing to melt.

Placement of the stove in your house can determine where and how heat is available, how much is stored (or lost through walls or windows), and ease of stoking and fuel storage. For instance, a stove used a lot for cooking might be close to the food preparation, one mainly for lounging—guess where—in the lounge of course! Carrying in firewood can be messy, so you can reduce floor sweeping by locating the feed tube close to the door.

Components and dimensions of an 8-inch rocket mass heater.

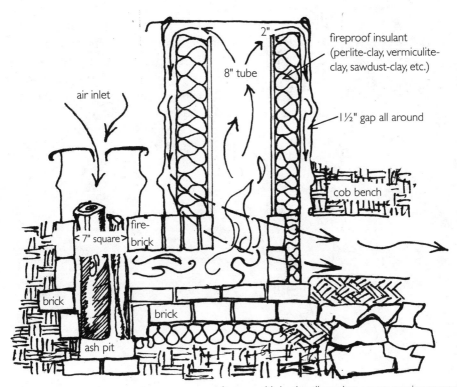

air inlet

2"

8" tube

fireproof insulant
(perlite-clay, vermiculite-clay, sawdust-clay, etc.)

1½" gap all around

cob bench

fire-brick

7" square

brick

brick

ash pit

Arrows with broken lines show gases passing around the barrel.

DIRECTING THE HEAT

There are variables which change where the heat is delivered. You can divide the heat that your stove generates according to your needs. There will be a trade-off between fast radiant heat and a long-lasting thermal battery. What heats up quickly—for example, a radiant barrel with little insulation around it—also cools down quickly. Conversely, what heats up slowly cools down slowly, so that the system with its pipe sunk several inches into a massive bed or couch provides warm comfort all night, hours after the fire has gone out. Decide well in advance what proportion you would like to have available for cooking, fast convective heat in your house, direct radiant heat that you can sit in front of, or contact heat that you sit, sprawl or lie on.

For instance, to maximize cooking efficiency, keep the top of the heat riser close to the barrel, about two inches. You will create a circular hot spot in the middle of the barrel top. For most usable radiant heat, leave a wider sleeve inside the barrel on the side where you would be sitting and pinch the sleeve in other directions. For a quick warm-up in the room you could build a taller heat riser with a bigger radiant barrel, possibly welding two barrels together end-to-end or using another conveniently sized metal container.

If radiant heat is prevented from escaping from the barrel, more heat will flow into storage. Part or all of the barrel can be encased in cob, and/or the barrel could be replaced by cob or brickwork. Thus, a bigger proportion of your heat will be available for storage and contact heat. You may want to size storage and the length of buried flue with that in mind.

If the wall behind the stove and bench is not well insulated, incorporate insulation between bench and wall and extra insulation behind the stove. Temperatures probably won't be high, but avoid foams as they may outgas. A couple of inches of clay-vermiculite, clay-perlite, or even clay-sawdust would be sufficient.

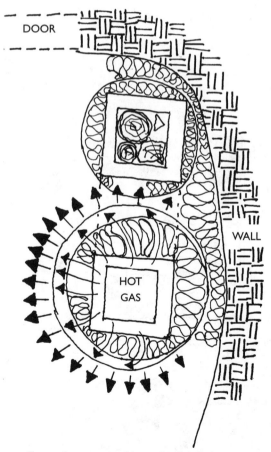

DOOR

HOT GAS

WALL

Eccentric gap around heat riser/insulation to favor radiant heat into the room. Serious insulation against exterior wall.

The Thermal Battery

Working with cob* offers structural flexibility like nothing else. Here is a medium which is eminently sculptable because you apply it handful by handful. The shapes are as limitless as anything you can build with clay, though you should avoid sharp corners, which can break off easily.

The shape you end up making your heat storage can be elegant and eloquent, whimsical yet grounded and comfortable, in conformation with your body's geometry.

The heat storage—the thermal battery—works best by slowly heating while there's a fire burning. Then that heat disperses throughout the mass, and finally heat leaves slowly, mostly by contact and convection, mostly at the points where and when you want it to leave. Total storage is limited by weight, not volume, so use heavy materials packed tight around the heat transfer ducts, then lighter, better insulated materials to enclose the whole thing.

The best way to achieve the thermal mass required is to use rock or broken concrete mortared together with a sand-clay mix without straw. If the bench is made entirely of cob it will have substantially less heat storage capacity than one that is largely stone.

On the other hand, the *proportion of available heat* you can extract from the hot gases depends upon the length, surface area and number of ducts exposed to the gas. Both the length and the diameter of the heat transfer ducts within the storage are critical.

Placing the Pipe

The longer the run of duct inside your bench, the more heat you can extract from the combustion gases. For more even distribution of heat across a wide bed, you can loop the ducts back and forth or run more than one from a common feed, reuniting them later. Bench systems with 30 feet of pipe work well and can reduce

the exit temperature of the gas to as low as 100°F, thus storing a very high proportion of the heat generated. For example, the 7-inch pipe in one of the benches at the North American School of Natural Building in Coquille Oregon is 31 feet long. When it's burning really hot, I can actually lick the exhaust pipe, to the amazement of visitors.

To rescue most of the heat, a 6-inch system should have at least 20 feet of internal duct, and a thermal mass of about three tons. An 8-inch system needs 30 feet of duct and should weigh about 5 tons. If you have a suspended floor, the extra weight will probably need additional structural support so your floor doesn't sag.

If you have a masonry slab floor, positioning the heat transfer duct low down can utilize the mass of the floor for extra heat storage.

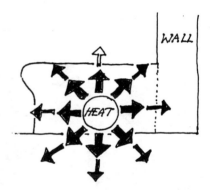

Exhaust tube sunk low in center of bench allows more heat storage in the bench (above). With the exhaust tube located higher (below), the surface of the bench is hotter, but less heat is stored and the bench cools faster.

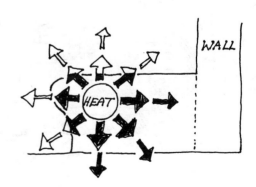

* See Glossary

Heat travels through cob at about an inch per hour and through rock about twice that fast. The duct that carries the hot gases through the bench can be positioned high to deliver fairly fast heat in a limited area or to store more heat for longer periods by being buried deeper into the bench. The effect is more noticeable with a wider bench. For instance, a duct with two inches of cob above it would provide a hot strip about two hours after the stove is lit. A bench 16 inches deep with a 6-inch duct 2 inches below the surface is left with 7 inches beneath it to be heated, so less is stored for a shorter period because heat is being lost faster and earlier from the surface. A duct that is too close to the surface can also make the bench uncomfortably hot along a line above the duct, yet quite chilly to either side. Our first Rocket Stove had a six-inch duct only two to three inches below the surface. In order to store sufficient heat

to warm the building adequately in very cold weather, we once got the bench so hot that it set fire to the cotton padding in the futon on top of it. If you plan to have a thick matress or cushions on top of the heated bench, keep hot ducts deep in the body of the bench -- six inches, if possible.

Generally, it is advisable to set the duct work fairly low in the bench. This will give more even heating, and retain heat a lot

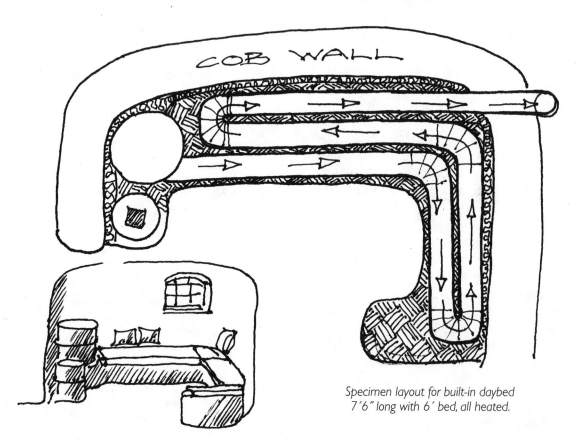

Specimen layout for built-in daybed 7´6″ long with 6´ bed, all heated.

longer especially as ash that accumulates in it will be at the bottom. Ash is an excellent insulator, so less heat travels downward than up or to the sides, unless the duct is always scrupulously clean. There's no necessity for the duct to continuously rise towards the exit. In fact if you wish, you can bring it up close to the surface, then to create a hot spot in the bench for rapid warm up, drop it again.

Sizing Built-in Furniture

Wall benches are comfy at 18 inches deep (front-to-back), though tolerable at 15 inches and should be 14 to 18 inches high. A lower bench has less capacity to store heat. You could accomplish both heated bench and bed by designing a bed that tapers at the foot and is widest at the shoulders. For seating, the bench is most comfortable if it is widest at the top of the seat, being undercut 3 to 5 inches, so there is space for your heels when you are sitting down. Make allowance for the overhang when you begin building.

If against a wall, a heated bed should be at least 7 feet long, 2½ feet wide (single) or 4½ feet (double). If free-standing both should be wider. At 7 ^{x} 4½ ^{x} 1½ feet it would weigh about 2½ tons. A 1½ foot wide bench 15 inches high would need to be 10 to 12 feet long to weigh one ton. In either case, a deep-set exhaust duct on top of a mass floor could substantially increase the effective amount of heat stored. You will first need to decide what power output and heating capacity you will build, based on exhaust duct diameter. Experience so far suggests that using the model described, a six-inch exhaust duct will heat only a tiny space in a rather mild climate, say, where temperatures don't normally drop below 20°F. In colder temperatures or in a larger house, you need an 8-inch system. We give step-by-step instructions for building an 8-inch system. If the system is bigger than you need, you can always simply run it for less time, but a too-small system is more difficult to remedy.

PLANNING THE EXIT FLUE

Rocket Stove chimneys behave differently from those of most wood stoves. When they are operating properly, gas temperatures are so low at their exit that fire danger is almost zero, but because of these low temperatures, water vapor in the stack is more likely to condense with creosote in solution at times. Higher efficiency of both combustion and heat use means a generally lower output of gases so the slower passage of cool moist gases contributes even more to condensation. Unprotected steel corrodes very quickly if it is uninsulated, or exposed to rain, or if its inside surface is not galvanized.

Consider carefully where the exhaust pipe will exit the building and where its outdoor end will be. Because a Rocket Stove pushes gas along the exhaust flue, there will be pressure inside the flue trying to squeeze gas out through any cracks. At some point of the burn, there may be C0 and N0$_x$ present, both very toxic. So, if you leave any exposed metal pipe inside the building, seal the joints very thoroughly with high-temperature silicone or high-temperature tape, to make really sure no gas can escape. With clip-together stovepipe, seal all along the clip joint as well as the connections between pipes. Then test for leakage by building a very smoky fire and blocking the exit at the top of the flue.

With *extremely* low temperatures (below 100°F in some cases) it is possible to end the stack in a position where rain will seldom reach it, under a lean-to roof or under the eaves.

If the stack is more than a few feet from the stove the exit gas will have cooled enough that there's no fire danger, so normal precautions for insulating an exit stack or isolating it from flammable materials may not apply. For other precautions, see the chapter called Fire! Fire! on page 58.

Make particularly sure the clean-outs and primer hole are well sealed. Any small crack downstream of the heat exchange barrel could leak dangerous gases, especially if the

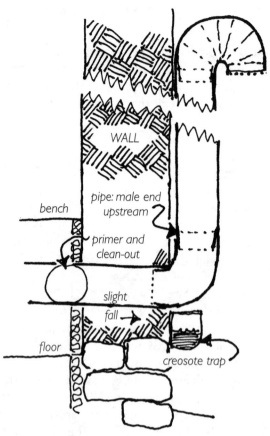

WALL

bench

pipe: male end
upstream

primer and
clean-out

slight
fall →

floor

creosote trap

*Make sure the flue tilts down to the
outdoors, that male ends of pipes are
upstream (not necessarily up the pipe
vertically) and that there's a primer just
inside the building.*

flue is long and/or you have an uninsulated exterior exhaust pipe. If you have any doubts at all it's probably worth investing in a carbon monoxide detector. They are inexpensive and easy to find.

As for locating the flue outside the building your main enemy is wind, particularly in sudden gusts. It's hard to predict where this may be a problem so have an alternate plan if there's even a suggestion of smoke backing up into the house. Consider relocating the pipe completely on the downwind side of the house, or making it much taller or using a commercial wind cowl on the top. If there is a known prevailing wind at times when you'll be using your stove, try not to exit your stovepipe on that side of your house.

Following a long run through a bench, the exit gas temperature should be very low

and there should be very little smoke. So it's possible to end the pipe in a sheltered position such as under the eave of the building. Mount an elbow on the top of the pipe and point it slightly downward to stop rain accumulating in the stack. A piece of ¼" hardware cloth over the end of the flue will prevent animals climbing in.

Chris and Jenn Reinhart use the commercially bought T-connectors, arranged as a letter H. See more about the Reinharts' stove in Case Studies.

Ernie Wisner has used a galvanized steel bucket set over the end of the flue, with slots cut into the pipe for gas escape.

*Preventing
blowback*

Some things to consider about chimneys:

Q. Should I exit the building down low or keep the stack inside as long as possible to strip a little more heat from it?

A. Well, if your flue temperature is already low at the end of the heat storage, say under 120°F, there really is little advantage to keeping the flue indoors. Take it out. Complications from creosote, toxic gas leaks, chimney fires, etc are much better dealt with outside a building.

Q. Should I go all out and build a masonry chimney or just settle for metal pipe?

A. Masonry chimneys take a lot of materials and labor. They are a potential entry point for rainwater. In earthquakes, they are often the only things to fall down. Our preference is for a good quality metal pipe, though it may not be as durable.

Q. Should I put a chimney damper at the end of the stack?

A. NO. Don't install a chimney damper! It can cause carbon monoxide to back up into the room.

Materials and Tools You'll Need
for an 8-inch flue system with a cob bench for heat storage

MATERIALS
Bricks, about 60–70 for the entire combustion chamber. If you don't use brick for the heat riser, 30–40 should do it.

Clay or clay soil
Sand } for cob and cob mortar

Straw (½ bale) or dead grass

15–17 gallon barrel for the feed tube

30 or 55 gallon barrel for the heat exchanger

8" diameter stovepipe/metal duct

Insulation: vermiculite, perlite or pumice (a 4 cu. ft. bag is plenty)

Insulation container: Water heater tank or ⅛" wire mesh (metal screen) or metal roofing, or sheet metal

Scraps of ⅛" or ¼" hardware cloth (optional)

Urbanite, rock or brick for heat storage

Alternative heat riser/burn tunnel: ¼" thich steel pipe, 2" shorter than interior of barrel, same diameter as ducting (exhaust system).

TOOLS that are essential
Shovel

Mattock or pick

Buckets

Wheelbarrow

Sharp pocket knife

Builder's level, 2 feet to 4 feet long

Measuring tape

OTHER TOOLS that you might need
Plastic tarp, about 8 x 10 feet

Hammer, cold chisel

Brick hammer, brick chisel

Mason's trowel

Chimney thermometer (magnetic, stick-on type)

Tinsnips, pliers

Old window screen (for sifting sand)

Rags

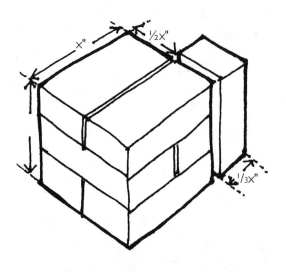

Most bricks have proportional dimensions.
Firebrick notably so.

They should be clean of mortar and without bulges or parts missing and they should be quite similar in size. Clean off lime mortar by rubbing two together, grinding every face flat. Or use a machete, flat blade or brick hammer first. Note that many bricks are made to modular proportions to fit together in all dimensions. Thickness is about a third of length; width about a half, allowing for mortar joints. Old bricks were not necessarily made to standard dimensions and different manufacturers each had their own size. Any irregularities should be readily apparent. The more irregular your bricks are, the more mortar it will take to keep them apart as you build. You'd like to limit mortar thickness because brick is stronger than mortar and you want to minimize the weakness inherent to mortar joints.

Bricks

From the bottom of the feed tube to the top of the heat riser, temperatures are intense. Temperature change happens very suddenly so the materials need to withstand sudden thermal shock, and of course need not to melt or burn at up to 2000°F. We have tried a lot of different materials and in general find the most durable to be soft common brick or a thick-walled steel pipe. Sooner or later most bricks seem to crack and break up in the extremely stressful conditions inside the area of combustion. Firebricks are perhaps more durable but quite costly, especially lower density kiln grade which is the better insulator. Soft common brick seems to work well, is easy to cut, and is often more resistant to cracking, particularly really old, low fired orange colored soft brick. But old bricks can be of irregular size and shape so make sure you have matching sizes.

Make sure you have sufficient bricks in good enough condition to do the job. Most of them will need to be intact, though you may be able to use partial bricks in places.

Clay

Clay can be found in the ground within about a mile of most places in North America. It will probably be mixed with sand, silt, organic matter and possibly stones. For making mortar, you will need wet clay, pressed through a $1/16$" screen or metal fly screen to remove rocks and impurities. For the combustion unit, that is, the stove itself, you'll need no more than five gallons. In the unlikely event that you can't find native clay, you could buy potter's clay from a ceramic supply store or ask your local potter for unwanted scraps. Or buy a bag of powdered "fire clay" from the building supply store. It performs better at high temperature and is easy to mix for mortar.

For building the cob parts of the heat storage, such as a built-in seat or bed, the clay may not need to be screened. If your clay soil is rich and sticky, you could need up to a ton or so (about 25 five gallon buckets) to build a heat storage bench or bed. If the soil has less clay, you will need more of it, but would need less sand to stabilize it and prevent cracking.

Sand

For mortar, you need a bucket full of $1/16"$ screened washed **mason's sand**, which you could either buy from a building supply store or screen yourself from cheaper coarser mixed sand. Don't use fine sand from beaches or sand dunes. It doesn't lock together well. Additionally, if you are building the heat storage with clay-rich soil, you'll need **builder's sand**—sometimes called **concrete sand** or **fill sand**—and you'll need quite a lot, depending on the size of the storage unit. It is normally sold by the cubic yard and you can expect a cubic yard to weigh over a ton, so don't put more than half a yard in a half-ton pick-up truck. Start with half a yard and see if that's sufficient. You can always get more later.

Barrels

To contain the hot gases issuing from the top of the heat riser, we often use a simple steel barrel, though people have used water heater tanks, garbage cans, or custom built cob or brick cylinders. You can regulate the amount of heat that the barrel gives up by the size of container you choose, and by whether parts of it are enclosed by a thermal buffer of cob, brick, etc.

To contain the fuel that sticks up from the feed tube, those 15 to 18-gallon grease drums that you sometimes see in gas stations or truck repair shops are ideal. Some have a press-down lid with rounded tabs all the way around the edge. Take out the rubber gasket. Usually, there's a two-inch bunghole in the center with a threaded cap that you can screw in or take out. Most Rocket Stoves with eight-inch flue size get just the right amount of oxygen to sustain a clean burn with the lid on and the bung open.

Used barrels are available many places. You shouldn't have to pay more than about fifteen bucks for a really good quality 55-gallon barrel. It might be worth trying one with a detachable clamp-on lid for ease of inspection, cleaning, etc. Try your local

Just barrels, in this case two 55 gallons, a 25, and a 17, often unwanted and in good shape.

dump, bulk food stores or caterers, building materials reuse stores, second-hand stores, scrap metal places and old industrial sites. Other sources include yard sales (ask, because they won't have them up front with the clothes and books), suppliers of honey or cooking oils, service stations and mechanics. 55-gallon barrels are easy to find, but in some areas, smaller ones are scarce, as plastics take over the barrel industry. The feed barrel isn't essential to a good stove; you could fashion it from sheet metal fairly easily, or use part of a hot water tank.

Barrels are highly likely to be painted and may have residues of what they contained. It's necessary that you burn off the paint before you get them inside the building, ideally in a good hot bonfire. Stay upwind and wear a respirator, as both the exterior paint of a barrel (not to mention the mysterious substance on the inside) can be toxic. Think about who is downwind. Clean out as much residue as you can before you burn them and make sure the bungs are detached before they get near the fire. After burning, use very coarse sandpaper from an industrial sanding belt to take off any remaining paint. You can use it with or without the belt sander.

Can a barrel melt in these temperatures? We haven't seen it happen yet. The melting point of the steel used in the typical oil drum is a much higher temperature than the stove will achieve.

Stovepipe

You'll need pipe to form the tunnels in your heat storage, or you could build a brick tunnel. The tunnel, however, does need to have a smooth interior surface so that the gases can flow along it gracefully, without being slowed by the drag of the walls. So the best option is to build your bench, bed, etc around metal duct work or stovepipe. Of preference, choose pipes bigger than you think you need, rather than smaller; they will get effectively smaller over time as ash, soot and dust accumulate.

Pipe diameters should be the same throughout and it's helpful to have adjustable elbow sections for changes of direction. Measure the diameter in advance, occasionally you will find a piece of $5\,^3/4"$ in the 6" pile, for instance, and they won't quite fit together. You need a tight fit to prevent the chance of carbon monoxide escaping through cracks in your masonry.

Preferably the pipe should be circular in section, not square. For strength, use steel or aluminum. You're going to leave it inside the furniture, so it's best if it's not painted, as some paints will burn off at bench temperatures and could escape through cracks in the cob.

Hot gases spiral up a flue. A round flue will carry more gas, more smoothly.

Buying new stovepipe can be expensive, so go to your local building reuse place, or a rural dump, or try yard sales, second-hand stores or dumpsters where demolition is happening. The pipe doesn't have to be in perfect condition, even small holes, dents, etc will be okay. Reuse stores in some places are not allowed to sell certain used stovepipe back to the public, so I have been asking stove contractors and dealers to save their used pipe for me, which would otherwise be thrown away. It should be possible to buy old 6 or 8-inch pipe for less than a dollar a foot. New stove pipe is quite expensive, particularly the triple wall variety, while air-conditioning or heater duct is cheaper.

High Temperature Insulation

Thermal insulation uses trapped air to prevent the passage of heat. The more air in a substance, the better it insulates, witness your down-filled parka or thermal sleeping bag. Thus the insulation you use should be as light as possible. There are three materials that we have found work well to insulate the heat riser in a rocket stove: lightweight pumice and vermiculite and/or perlite mixed with clay slip. All three are fairly easy to find, inexpensive and simple to use, although both vermiculite and perlite may give off dust, so use a respirator when mixing them. The clay slip helps to bond the lightweight dusty particles together and to hold a shape. Buy the coarsest grade of perlite you can find. Sources would include masonry building materials suppliers. Avoid horticultural suppliers, as horticultural grade perlite is very porous and takes up a lot of water.

Perlite comes in big plastic bags. We get four cubic feet for around ten dollars. You might need two bags for a 55-gallon stove, a single bag for a smaller one. Make up a clay slip by mixing clay and water very thoroughly. You can do this with your bare hands, with a paint paddle on an electric drill, or with a wooden paddle. I like the bare hands method; I enjoy the feel of the clay between my fingers. The mixture should be thick enough that after you dip your fingers in it you cannot see your fingerprints. Mix slip with perlite at 1 measure of slip to 6–9 parts of perlite. Dump a few gallons of perlite onto a tarp or into a wheelbarrow and sprinkle the clay slip over the pile as broadly as you can. Tumble the pile with your bare hands or a shovel or by rolling the tarp. Try different methods. The idea is to get the white grains dirty all over, totally clothed in clay. It may take quite a lot of time to get it completely mixed. When you're through, you should be able to pat together a little snowball of the mixture and have it stay intact on the surface of your palm. Don't use any more clay than you have to because clay is denser than perlite and will reduce the insulating qualities of the mix. And don't compact the mix in tumbling it or in setting it into the stove. Compaction will reduce the insulative value of the mix.

Insulation Containers

Most fireproof insulation is either in the form of loose-fill or sheets of fiber. Both need to be contained, even if you mix clay with perlite or vermiculite. You will create a cylinder of wire mesh or of sheet metal, or perhaps use a ready-made container such as an old water heater tank with the ends cut off. Used materials should be quite adequate, obtainable from scrap metal merchants or at your local dump or used building materials centers.

Steel Pipe

If you choose to use a pipe for the heat riser, the best source is usually a scrap metal place. Sometimes they will cut it to length. It should be at least 1/8" and preferably 1/4" thick. Pipe can be round or square, but note that a square tube of the same cross-sectional area won't carry gas quite as fast, so for an 8" round flue you might use an 8" square heat riser. If you choose steel for the burn tunnel or feed tube, be aware that where oxygen is plentiful it will gradually burn away.

Several people have experimentally used triple-wall stainless steel pipe. Its durability in Rocket Stove use is not known, but its thermal mass is low and its insulation value is high. So it could be a valuable material to use. It makes narrower heat exchange barrels possible. In some areas triple wall is available second-hand.

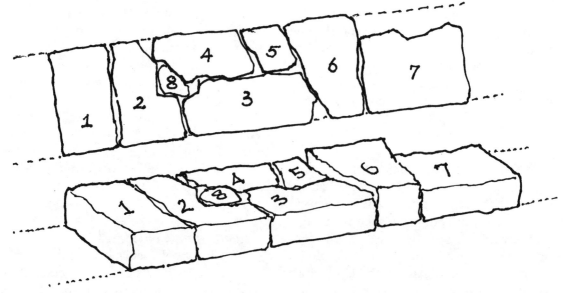

Selecting Urbanite. Choices in order of preference are: (1) Parallel sides, right angle corners, good face on each side of wall, rectangular. (2) Two good faces, three right angles, large. (3) One long good face. Half-width of wall, large. (4) Medium long face, half-width of wall. (5) Small, half-width of wall. (6) Less desirable: two good faces, but stone is thicker or thinner than most (problems laying next course). (7) Big and a good face, 3 right angles, but being about ¾ wall thickness, difficult to add to alongside. (8) No good faces, but can be used as infill.

Urbanite

Urbanite is a common mineral found mostly in cities. When sidewalks, driveways, patios and garden paths are broken up, chunks of concrete are often hauled off to a landfill dump or recycled to make gravel. Urbanite is very common in the waste stream and sometimes can be delivered free to your site or is at least free for the taking, saving the owner a dump fee. Look for 3", 4" or 5" thick chunks. Really thick urbanite is too heavy to handle and when there is rebar or wire mesh reinforcement in it, it's too hard to break. Go with a sledgehammer and goggles, you may need to break it up at the source. For ease of layout, try to choose pieces that are the width of your wall, or about half that width, nothing in between. Take pieces as big as you can handle. A wide 2-inch thick board about 8 feet long makes it easy to slide heavy pieces into your vehicle. Urbanite is very heavy, so the economics of hauling long distance soon get to be an issue. Look for it close to your building site.

Straw

Straw is the fiber portion of cob that gives the material its tensile strength. There are many sources of straw: Animal feed supplies (be sure to get straw, not hay). The cheapest way is to find cast-offs from carnivals, country fairs, and large strawbale house building contractors who have purchased extra. Used horse bedding, although it may contain urine or dung, will make excellent cob. Just make sure straw bales haven't gotten wet, as straw can rot and cause problems. A bale can cost from $4 to $12.

Dimentia and Proportia

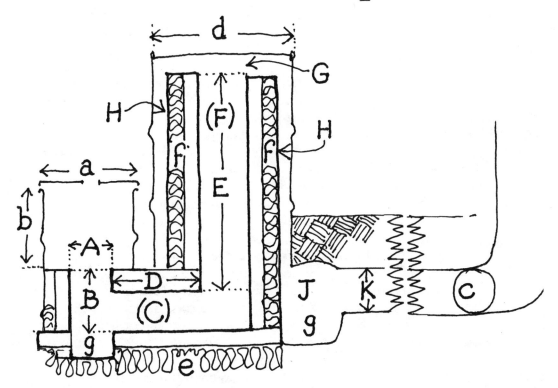

A few dimensions and relative proportions are critical to your rocket stove working at all. Some others are not crucial, but are strongly recommended. The dimensions of critical importance are keyed in the diagrams on this page and on page 38 with large, bold capital letters. Some dimensions are not critical; we note that too. Throughout this section, we'll describe the dimensions and proportions of a basic downdraft self-feeding cooking and heating rocket stove with a 55-gallon drum heat riser and an 8-inch stovepipe flue. Refer to the diagrams on page 38 and double-check all of the numbers and letters before you begin building.

A is the cross sectional area of the feed tube. It should be kept *very tight*. Note that an 8-inch pipe at **K** gives you about 50 square inches, so the cross sectional area of **A** would allow a hole about 7 inches square or 6 inches by 8 inches. (A 6-inch exhaust pipe can take about 6 inches by 5 inches, (30 square inches) at **A**. (The calculation for area within a circle is πr^2.)

B is the effective height of the feed tube, down which fuel self-loads by gravity. *Keep it short.* The fire should not burn all the way up the feed tube. In a well working stove there will be enough draw through the stove to keep combustion to the very bottom of that tube. The tube is best rectangular or square (not rounded), in cross section.

C is the area of the horizontal burn tunnel, normally made of brick, in which most of the burning happens. If convenient, make it slightly wider than high. A single brick on edge is about 4 inches high, so arrange bricks flat or on edge to make up the required height.

C should be the *tightest part* of the intestinal system. The size of the cross sectional areas of all parts of the stove's internal ducts or intestines *should never decrease below that of* **C**. In other words, the cross sectional areas of **F, G, H, J** and **K** should all be greater than that of **C**. Make sure you keep the cross sectional areas of the exhaust stack, the horizontal flues, and the gap at the top of the heat riser bigger than the area of combustion at **C** to avoid bottlenecks which could slow combustion or back up smoke into the room.

D is the distance from the feed tube to the heat riser and should normally be as short as possible to minimize heat loss and increase the barrel temperature. Optimum proportion is about half the height of the heat riser. Longer tunnels will need more insulation.

E is the most important single dimension. **E** is the height from the bottom of the feed tube to the top of the heat riser. **E** affects how much air the stove is able to suck through the fuel and therefore the rate of burning, the potential power output, the temperature of the cooking surface, and also radiant heat production from the sides of the barrel. Draw is proportional to height, so if **E** were twice as high, you would have twice the draw. The height in the specimen 8-inch system shown is 33 inches, but could be anywhere from 25 to 50 inches.

F is the cross sectional area of the heat riser and should be not less than **C**. The heat riser can be 7 inches by 7 inches square or 8 inches diameter round.

G is a little hard to describe. It's an imaginary cylinder rising from the top of the heat riser to the roof of the barrel. The total area of the walls of that cylinder should also be greater than the area of **C** to avoid slowing the gas flow at this point. With an 8" system, its height should be 2" to 3". (With a 6" system, it should be 1½" to 2").

H needs to be about 1½" wide. For even heating from all sides of the barrel, we need to encourage the hot gases to swirl down equally all around the barrel, not just short-cut to the exit tube. It's good to place the barrel eccentrically over the heat riser with the gap slightly wider on a side where you want extra radiant heat and make the gap narrowest where you want the least heat.

J is an easy place to unwittingly create a bottleneck. Make sure to bell out the cross-sectional area at this point, with a good deep ash pit so that ash build-up doesn't constrict the flow. **K** is the exhaust, the horizontal flue that carries hot gas through your floor, heated bench, bed etc. This should be at least the size of the heat riser (8" to 10" diameter) or it could be made of more than one duct, totaling a much bigger cross sectional area, as for instance, if you're using it to heat a floor. Any abrupt turns in the stove's intestines will somewhat slow the flow of gases, so try to make elbows less than 90 degrees or a larger diameter than straight runs.

The following dimensions are less important but please read the notes.

a is the diameter of the 15 to 18-gallon barrel, which encloses the feed tube. **a** will be in the region of 14".

b is the additional height the feed barrel rises above the feed tube. Keep it less than a foot, or there's a danger that hot gases can accumulate in that space and reduce the efficiency of the draw. It is, however, valuable to install this barrel, which makes it easy to control occasional stray smoke, and to regulate the air input to the stove.

c is a primer/clean-out hole. Put it as close as possible to the bottom of the vertical stack.

d is the diameter of the heat riser barrel. A standard 25-gallon steel barrel is 18½" across; a standard 55-gallon is 22½". 25 or 30-gallon barrels work well with a 6-inch duct system and a 55-gallon barrel does fine with an 8-inch system. The bigger the barrel, the lower its surface temperature will be.

e is the insulation beneath the burn tunnel. To keep the temperature in the heat riser as high as possible, you'll need 2" to 3" of insulation here. If you wish to store some of the heat generated in the floor beneath the stove, leave out the insulation.

f is the insulation thickness around the heat riser. Put in as much insulation as you have space for.

g is a clean-out. Make the opening big enough that you can get a cleaning brush in. Flare the clean-out into the duct so you can reach your arm in there.

Constructing the Combustion Unit

Once you've decided how high in the room you want the barrel to be, you can decide on the floor level of the burn tunnel (which can be below, at, or above the floor level of the room). You may want to plan for a few inches of insulation below the burn tunnel. The insulation (**e** in the cross-sectional drawing on page 35) and the brick ash pit (at **c**) could be inset into the floor or laid on top. To recess stove parts into the floor is a lot easier if you build stove before floor. The floor of the burn tunnel should be level, flat, solid, and at least two feet in any direction including downwards from any burnable parts of the building. ***Don't build directly on a wooden floor or up against a wooden wall.*** Also be sure not to place the barrel or feed tube beneath anything in the room that may present a fire hazard, such as overhead shelves.

Mortar

You will be using a mortar that you can compound yourself or you can buy commercial fireplace mortar. To make your own, you'll need mason's sand (that means fine grained, sharp sand) and fairly pure clay. Unless you buy commercial clay, put both of them through a ⅛" or ¹/₁₆" screen or a fly screen, to eliminate lumps on which the bricks could teeter. Mix in advance about a bucket full of mortar, that is, four to six gallons, at about one part clay to four or five parts sand. Clay mortar will keep as long as it is damp. Don't use cement-based mortar unless it's fire cement mixed with clay. Most cement is non-refractory and would be likely to break up rapidly under the thermal shock it would experience. The same may be true of lime or gypsum-based mortars, whereas clay merely becomes fired and in fact itself turns into a brick-like material.

A Mock-Up

Begin by laying out your bricks on any unburnable flat level surface, preferably outdoors just to practice how they might go together. I would recommend that you build a mock-up—without mortar—of the entire brick structure, not necessarily in the final position, and fire it up really hot to make sure it works.

For the feed tube and the heat riser tower, use bricks on edge to keep the tower as thin as possible so it doesn't take forever soaking up heat, and to leave plenty of space for insulation. Bricks can be laid flat and/or on edge in various combinations in the base and along the burn tunnel to get the interior height of the burn tunnel right.

It helps to use bricks exactly the same height for each course (not a concern if you have perfect new identical bricks). Easier than measuring them and more precise is to lay them out on a really flat surface such as a straight board or a concrete floor, a dozen or so at a time.

Sometimes instead of using bricks we build the heat riser with *thick* steel pipe (⅛" or ¼"), and recently, people have used triple-wall insulated stainless steel. Solid pipe is very durable, but triple-wall we can't vouch for.

Sorting Bricks: A, F, H and L are all the same height. B, E, I and M are a different height but are equal. Each group of four will make a course of the heat riser.

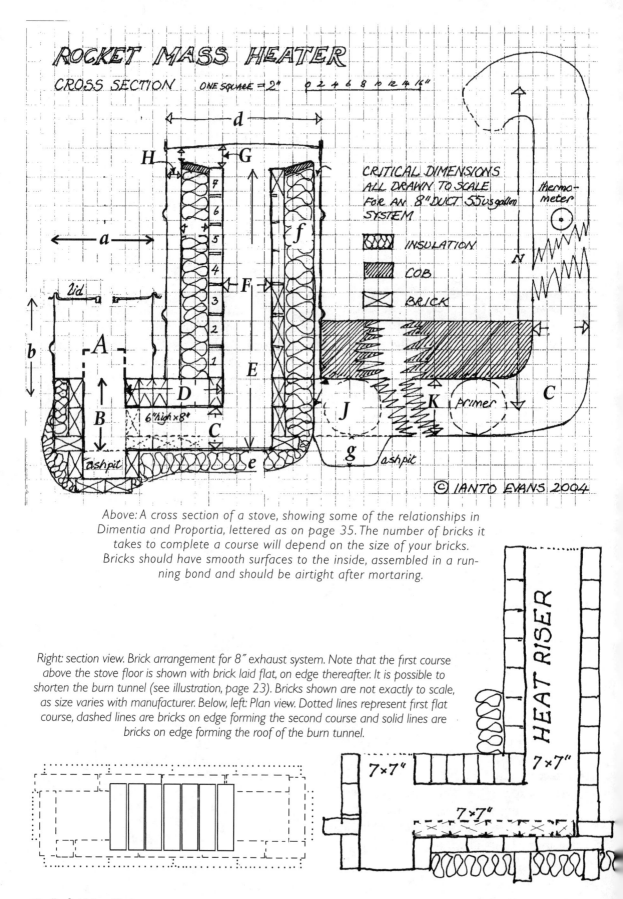

ROCKET MASS HEATER

CROSS SECTION   ONE SQUARE = 2"   0 2 4 6 8 10 12 14 16"

CRITICAL DIMENSIONS
ALL DRAWN TO SCALE
FOR AN 8" DUCT 55 us gallon
SYSTEM

INSULATION

COB

BRICK

thermo-meter

lid

ashpit

6" high x 8"

ashpit

Primer

© IANTO EVANS 2004

Above: A cross section of a stove, showing some of the relationships in Dimentia and Proportia, lettered as on page 35. The number of bricks it takes to complete a course will depend on the size of your bricks. Bricks should have smooth surfaces to the inside, assembled in a running bond and should be airtight after mortaring.

Right: section view. Brick arrangement for 8" exhaust system. Note that the first course above the stove floor is shown with brick laid flat, on edge thereafter. It is possible to shorten the burn tunnel (see illustration, page 23). Bricks shown are not exactly to scale, as size varies with manufacturer. Below, left: Plan view. Dotted lines represent first flat course, dashed lines are bricks on edge forming the second course and solid lines are bricks on edge forming the roof of the burn tunnel.

HEAT RISER

7×7"

7×7"

7×7"

Insulation Under the Stove

Build the permanent model on a hard, flat, level base, preferably brick. Whether to use insulation beneath and around the burn tunnel depends upon whether you want to use the ground beneath the stove as thermal storage or if you are more interested in having your stove heat up quickly. If, for instance, one function of your stove is to heat tea water, then you would want to rush the hot gases through the system losing as little heat along the way as possible.

On the other hand, if the stove is to be used only for space heating or charging up a heat storage bench or even for slow cooking, then it might be in your interests to allow the ground beneath your floor to heat and slowly release that heat over time.

Bernhard Masterson suggests a diagonal cross support of bricks laid flat in the insulation beneath the heat riser to support the weight without crushing the insulation.

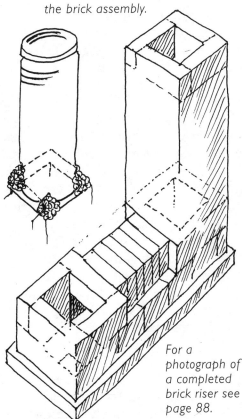

A steel tube is an option for heat riser material. Mud the corners onto the brick assembly.

For a photograph of a completed brick riser see page 88.

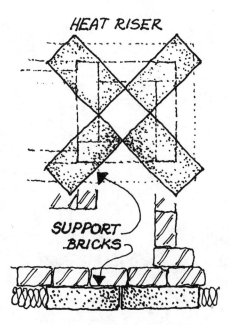

HEAT RISER

SUPPORT BRICKS

Infloor Insulation: Shows diagonal brick support for weight of the heat riser, (above in plan view) surrounded by mineral insulant (below, in section view).

Building the Brickwork

Set the first course of bricks very carefully. Their position and stability will affect how easy it is to build the whole structure. Mortar courses should be as thin as possible, ¼" or less. Arrange bricks so the corners interlock, without straight line vertical joints more than two bricks high. Check each course for level carefully as you build it. Check regularly for vertical with a builder's level. It's important. (More images on pages 42-47).

As you build, clean off surplus mortar that squeezes out between the bricks on the inside of the tower very carefully with a dry cloth without disturbing the stability. Finally, clean out the burn tunnel very thoroughly to remove every vestige of mortar that could affect the gas flow. Fuel needs to fall freely into the feed tube, so make sure there are no edges of bricks protruding into the tube.

You'll want the heat riser to extend up to close to the top of the barrel. So measure the height of the barrel in advance and make sure that the courses of brickwork fit that dimension closely. If the gap above the top of the heat riser is less than about 1½ inches, it may be too tight, so the combustion gases will have trouble with their exit. Conversely, if the gap is too deep, the cooking surface (the top of the barrel) may not get hot enough fast enough to cook on. To get just the right height, you have some flexibility in using thicker or thinner mortar courses and in how you support the barrel, using broken brick or tile plus the mortar seal.

It is possible to build the feed tube and burn tunnel out of brick and to use steel tube for the heat riser. Steel in that position will be much more durable than if it's used where there is more oxygen available further "upstream."

Adding Insulation

After the combustion chamber (including the heat riser) is constructed and any protruding mortar is smoothed off inside, you can apply the insulation. First build up a circular base on which both insulation and the heat exchange barrel will stand. Use whatever is to hand: broken brick, chunks of old concrete, rocks, etc. The base needs to be airtight, so cob everything together. Test for height with a level and tape measure.

The insulant mixture needs to be in a cylindrical container surrounding the heat riser and fitting within the heat exchange barrel, but extending down to the level of the bottom of the exit flue. A standard electric water heater tank is just about the right size if you cut off both ends. If you don't have a water heater tank, sheet metal can be rolled and wired together.

Recently, we've been using ⅛" or ¼" hardware cloth (steel mesh) formed into a rough cylinder and wired together. It's fairly easy to lightly pack the insulation inside it to maintain its cylindrical shape. At the top of the insulation, make a little cap of sand-clay

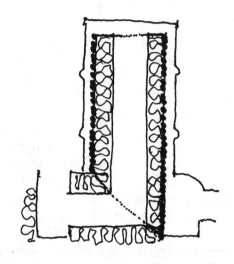

Insulation container. Note that the insulation in the container extends all the way down to the ash pit.

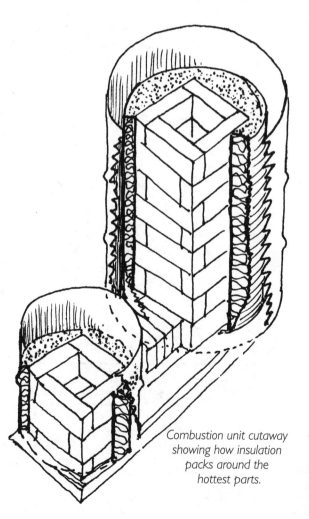

Combustion unit cutaway showing how insulation packs around the hottest parts.

up to the height of the top of the heat riser. It's important to **maintain the sides of the insulation container vertical** so as not to impede the flow of exit gases.

Remember that the bottom of the heat exchange barrel should be located higher than the exit duct or you will have to cut a hole in the side of the barrel to get the gas to flow out.

In order for gases to flow smoothly through the tight gap between barrel and flue as they enter the thermal mass, there needs to be extra space all around the bottom of the barrel, a ring-shaped channel that collects the falling hot gas and directs it to the flue. As this is a prime trap for lightweight ash, make it big enough that you could get your hand or a vacuum cleaner tube into most of it. This channel needs to extend all around the base of the barrel, dropping and widening from above the bridge to the clean-out/ash pit where the flue begins. Shape it in a sand-clay mixture without straw, leaving the sides and base really smooth, so that a clean-out tool can rake out ash without snagging.

Setting the Barrel

It takes two people to carefully lower the barrel over the heat riser. Be very cautious not to bump the heat riser and knock it out of alignment. Seal around the bottom of the barrel with sand-clay. Now test the stove by lighting a very hot fire and feeling for radiant heat off the side of it. Run your hand from top to bottom and around every side, slowly, a few inches from the barrel, feeling with the back of your hand for radiant heat. If there are any cool spots, or if one side is a lot cooler than another, you may need to pick up the barrel and reposition it to correct the situation.

Tips on Laying Brick

Brick will resist heat better than mortar, so keep mortar courses as thin as possible. The finer you sift the sand and clay, the thinner the mortar courses can be—a ¼" pebble means the course can't be less than ¼" thick.

Make sure bricks have no projections wherever they meet other bricks. Clean off old mortar carefully. Lime mortar will usually fall off easily; cement mortar is more difficult, it sticks tightly to the bricks and sometimes you'll break the brick trying to clean it off.

Spalls, cracks and chunks missing may not be a problem depending on location. Mix mortar wet about the consistency of guacamole or custard, so that it is easily worked. Clay-sand, unlike lime or cement, is kind to the skin, so you can apply it without tools, though if you have a mason's trowel, a bricklayer's trowel, try building your skill with it. Soak bricks in a container of water before use or they will suck water out of the mortar too fast. You have very little time to adjust, so try to set bricks level and plumb and in place the first time. Remember the mortar is there mostly to hold the bricks apart (to stop them rocking) not to glue them together. Before ending work each day or every couple of hours, stuff mortar into remaining cracks and holes, then smooth it all down with a coarse damp rag (burlap is ideal) or a big coarse plastic sponge.

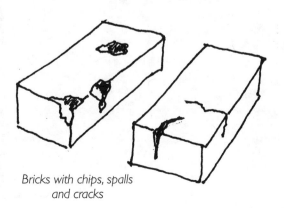

Bricks with chips, spalls and cracks

The first course of bricks in a mock-up directly on the ground. Bricks are laid flat, clean sides into the center for good gas flow. This shows the base of the burn tunnel. In the actual stove, this course is set on a flat smooth layer of brick. That layer of bricks may or may not be on a bed of insulation, depending on the design.

The first course determines the length of the burn tunnel, the horizontal leg of the "J." Note builder's level ready for use.

Level each course as you build. Maintain the same width all along the channel.

The second course is on edge;
check for vertical and square.
Lay bricks in a running bond,
each brick spanning a joint
below it.

Provided a good face of each brick
looks into the combustion zone,
imperfections in other parts of
bricks are less important.

The second course, one
brick short. The partial brick
at upper left will allow the
last brick to span the joint
below it.

The bridge of brick over the burn tunnel is a good place to put your better firebrick, stacked on edge in this case.

Below, left: Fourth course going up. Check for square, level and vertical.

The brickwork is ready to support a heavy steel heat riser.

Looking down the barrels of the feed tube and heat riser.

Left: Two Rocket Stoves side-by-side in an experimental session with heat risers of steel instead of brick. The brick fortresses around the burn tunnels form the supports for the heat exchange barrels as well as containment for the gases flowing down the barrels and into the exit flues, at right. The bricks and barrels' bottoms will be sealed from outside with cob.

The entire assembly ready for the horizontal flue. Brick and cob form the neck for the exhaust pipe. Make sure these are airtight junctions.

Photos this page: Kirk Mobert

The insulation around a steel heat riser in a greenhouse Rocket is contained by sheet metal, bent into a cylinder and held with wire. A sand-clay cap at the top few inches holds perlite in.

The completed system, ready for testing. Note steam escaping from exit flue.

A good example of a brick tower under construction
in Chris and Jenn Reinhart's house.
A fortress of brick is mortared in to support the barrel.
Photos, this page: Chris Reinhart.

The same stove, completed.

Building the Thermal Battery

Materials for Building a Bench, Couch or Bed

You will use rocks or urbanite (recycled concrete chunks), filling the gaps with cob. Cob is a mineral-fiber composite made by mixing together damp clay soil, sand and usually straw. The easiest way to make small quantities of it is to lay a tarp on the ground, dump the ingredients on it then roll and tread it together with your bare feet. The final consistency for heat storage should be very sandy and homogeneous, sticky and damp enough to hold together for hand sculpting. For a thorough explanation of cob see *The Cobber's Companion* or *The Hand-Sculpted House* (in Recommended Books).

Lay Out Exhaust

Draw out on your floor the shape of the heat storage you want to build. Set a layer of rocks in damp cob to begin with, and then place your exhaust pipe on top of the rocks.

The exhaust pipe may be made of metal duct or stove pipe, aluminum or steel. Lay out the pipes beginning at the stove end, facing the male ends of the connectors upstream, that is, towards the fire. This way, if there's a condensation drip in the outdoor part of the pipe, it can't run out at the joints, but can be caught in a creosote trap at the bottom of the vertical stack, where there should be a clean-out. If the flue passes outside through a wall, build it to drain outwards as protection against condensation running in from the outdoor stack. If you are simultaneously building a thermal battery and a cob wall, build in a pipe of equal or greater diameter than your system. You may need to reinforce a thin metal pipe to protect it from distortion caused by differential settlement in the wet cob. Make all pipe connections airtight to avoid carbon monoxide leaks.

CONNECTING STOVE TO BENCH

The three-dimensional shape of the transition from stove to bench is hard to describe, yet fairly easy to sculpt. Effectively, you're connecting a thin, partial cylinder to a fat cylindrical tube at right angles. English has no word for this geometry. The ideal material for the connection is a sand-clay mixture fairly rich in sand and stiff enough that it can't fall into the hole.

To simplify construction, use scraps of ¼" or ⅛" hardware cloth or expanded metal lath or scrap sheet metal. Curve the lath into place to fit the shape using several small pieces, and then plaster your sand-clay very carefully

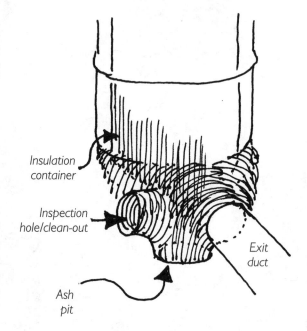

Insulation container

Inspection hole/clean-out

Exit duct

Ash pit

This shows the shape of the chamber.

over its surface. Add extra volume of space at this location, as it is a prime candidate for ash build-up and blockage. If possible leave an ash pit here up to one-gallon capacity.

An alternative—if less aerodynamic—approach is to rough out the box in brick, then plaster it inside and out with cob, really smooth. We have also used slate roofing tiles and flattish rocks. The result may look funky but will work fine if you emphasize **leaving plenty of space inside.**

Locate Clean-Outs

You will need to put an inspection hole close to where the pipe exits from the barrel and another one at the bottom of the vertical exhaust pipe. You may need others if your pipe has many bends and turns. The hole at the base of the vertical pipe doubles as a primer into which you may need to put burning newspaper to get the stove started in unusual weather conditions (see Light My Fire). Each inspection hole may also be used to clean out the flues. The simplest way to build them is to use a T-junction in standard duct work or stovepipe. Metal caps are made commercially to fit these pipes, or you could make a plug of your own design. Make this plug airtight to prevent carbon monoxide leaks into the room.

Sculpt the Thermal Battery

The cob immediately surrounding the pipe should be packed in really tight for good thermal contact and should contain no straw within six inches of the pipe. Pack cob very thoroughly between the rocks and tight against the stovepipe, working up the sides of the stovepipe evenly and carefully, adding rocks as you build. If the work is done with love and the bench is protected until it's dry, there's no danger of the pipes collapsing. Straw is only necessary in the cob that is close to the surface of the bench. Without the straw the cob may crack or be subject to shattering if it's hit with a heavy object, so put in a good amount for the surface layer, chopped to two inches in length. Protect the bench with a half-inch or so of a hard earthen plaster. Reinforce the corners of the bench, as they will get dinged and bashed with use. You may want to try a gypsum based plaster nearest the barrel as the metal will shrink and swell with the rise and fall of temperature, as will the clay. For more information on plasters and amendments, see *The Hand-Sculpted House* and *The Natural Plaster Book*, both in Recommended Books.

Feeding and Caring for Your Dragon

Wales, my native land, (which has been described as The Indian Reservation of the British Isles), has a 2000 year-plus cultural tradition of the importance of home and hearth. To this day the national plant is the leek and the national animal the Red Dragon, which graces our flag and is to be seen everywhere. It is well known that every cottage home had a house dragon, a cute little fellow who crouched in the inglenook, snoozing but perpetually alert to the need to start a fire and to warm the house. He is called *DRAIG GOCH*, (which almost rhymes with fried pork).

Rocket Stoves are the modern dragons, the living heaters that sleep in a corner, unless your house, like mine, has no corners. Like any well-behaved house dragon, mine never smokes (unless he's really young and just learning the hazards of smoking); he growls a little (or do dragons really just purr deeply?), but maintains a little warmth all through the cold northern winter, even when he shows no fire. And of course, unlike the rascally Oriental dragons that actually blow fire from their nostrils, all good Welsh dragons swallow their fire, discharging it with joyful flatulence.

LIGHT MY FIRE

If you're accustomed to lighting fires in box stoves, you're in for surprises. Rocket Stoves function almost diametrically opposite to any kind of stove you've ever lit. The wood stands upright, the air goes down, the kindling goes behind the paper and the firewood behind that. The feed tube cools itself so well that I can comfortably sit on the feed barrel in my house. Operation is a brief, very hot clean burn, then you seal the feed for heat stored in the "battery" to slowly warm your home.

First, make sure your draft is leaving the house, not back drafting up the feed tube. You can tell quite easily by blowing out a match close over the feed tube. Watch whether the smoke rises or if it falls into the burn tunnel. If the temperature of the bench gets colder than the outdoor air, a counter flow will carry air from outdoors down the exhaust pipe and through the intestines to exit up the feed tube. This is most likely to happen if you've been gone from your house for a long time in cold weather. Normally, though, you can expect the system to draw air into the stove.

Check your indoor stack thermometer. If it reads lower than the air in the room, you will need to prime the system by putting lighted newspaper into the base of the stack.

Use of Paper and Preparation for Lighting

Remember that it's the heat riser that makes this thing work, not the exhaust pipe. So in normal operation, to heat up the riser quickly, I like to first prepare two or three sheets of dry crumpled newspaper, (not tissue, thick paper, glossy paper or cardboard). With practice, you can get away with two full sheets. Try not to use more, as the clays in commercial paper don't burn and can rapidly build up an ash problem in your tunnels. Then I prepare a handful of very thin, very dry, straight kindling with all of the thin ends together, and the matches. I set them all down on the bench alongside of the stove. *Kindling needs to be tinder-dry.*

If there's any question about the dryness of the paper, kindling, or matches, I generally leave them in a warm place above or right up against the stove overnight so as to be dust dry in the morning. In damp climates such as the Maritime Pacific zone, a kindling shelf or rack above the stove is a good idea, but make sure nothing can fall off it onto the hazardously hot surface of the stove. Safer, perhaps, is to leave paper, kindling and matches on the heated bench.

(1) Now I light one of the newspaper crumples and reach down with it so I can stuff it into the horizontal combustion tube, blowing gently down the feed. I wait until the smoke

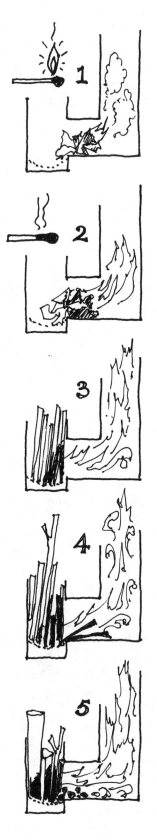

from it finds the heat riser and I hear it burning fiercely, then (2) I drop in the other newspaper crumples so that they are directly beneath the feed tube but in contact with the burning piece. If for any reason smoke comes up the feed tube, I just blow again gently to give it the right idea until it's drawing strongly up the heat riser.

Warning:

If you burn large quantities of paper, its lightweight ash may float down the stove's intestines and constipate it. After initial ignition, burn only wood.

Adding Kindling

Kindling must be tinder-dry all through, pencil-thin, straight, split, splintery and long enough that it can't fall down into the burn tunnel or feed tube. As the paper ignites, I very quickly stack a fistful of the thinnest kindling **vertically against the exit from the feed tube** so that the burning newspaper backs up to it. (3) The heat of the newspaper will ignite the kindling, which is burning upstream of it. Then I add more kindling, tight against the opening and upstream of the first load, which as it burns will eat its way back into the new kindling. (4) Now I add thicker pieces of wood until the feed tube is completely full; (5) the fire will chew backwards into progressively thicker fuel. Only the bottom end of the wood should be burning. **Always stoke behind the burning pieces,** load the feed tube from the end away from the burn tunnel and completely fill the feed tube. If you don't, your stove may smoke.

Ideally, as the bottom ends burn off the fuel, pieces will drop by gravity into the feed tube. Often they jam up so you may need to shake them down, sometimes quite vigorously. Logjams can be avoided somewhat by (a) choosing straight fuel without side branches, (b) not cutting fuel so long that it cantilevers itself out of the feed tube and (c) feeding fuel thick end **down** so it doesn't wedge itself into the feed.

Stoking

You can regulate the power output of the stove and therefore how hot the barrel gets by the thickness of the fuel. If you need sudden heat, use a handful of thin, split, really dry, straight kindling up to the size of a child's wrist. The thinner the fuel, the greater the power output and the faster the stove heats up. Conversely, if you want to be able to leave for a couple of hours and keep the fire burning, you can use thicker—and preferably denser—fuel. There's normally enough heat retained in a brick feed tube to keep one single log burning for a couple of hours. For cleanest burning, fires need to be hot and well stoked. Rockets work best if they are fired at full load for a few hours each day to charge up the thermal battery of the heat storage. As soon as the embers die down, close the lid as tightly as it will go. This stops the exhaust pipe from sucking warm air through the bench and cooling off your mass, and prevents heated air being dragged out of your house. If you choose to build a model without a closable lid, you may need to set some sort of slide damper at the top of the feed tube to regulate how fast the stove burns and also to control stray smoke from escaping. We use fire brick or tile, or a flat sheet of cast iron, which we remove for stoking.

THE FUEL YOU BURN

Keep it Dry

If firewood contains water, the energy produced by burning it is partly used up by boiling that water out of the wood. You lose efficiency dramatically by drying the wood out during burning. The steam so produced can condense inside your flues, rusting them out and dripping from loose joints and inspection holes. So make sure your wood supply is gathered in dry weather and stacked to season in a well-ventilated pile. If cut green, that is, from recently live trees, it should be split open before stacking to allow it to dry out thoroughly, preferably for a full year before burning. In damp climates, store firewood indoors to dry a little more before burning it. Make outdoor wood stacks high with the top covered to keep rain off and the sides open so that the breeze goes through. Thus wood can continue to dry even in damp weather. Don't throw a plastic sheet on a woodpile; it may trap moisture and condensation from the ground itself. You could end up with your firewood wetter than when you stacked it. If you have any doubts about the dryness of firewood, measure weight loss of a test sample by setting it on your stove overnight.

Kindling Selection

To test the suitability of deadwood as kindling, examine how strong it is. If it doesn't easily break across the grain, it probably has good fiber and will burn well. Kindling should be **straight, dry, very thin, split, roughly triangular, long enough to stand up in the feed tube, strong** (difficult to break), **fibrous.** It sometimes helps if there's a little pitch in kindling. Conifers such as Douglas fir, pine (except pitch pine), cedar and fir are excellent but avoid larch (tamarack), hemlock and spruce. It's tempting to gather twigs, but they have disadvantages. Twigs tend to be crooked, not straight, and they are covered in bark. Trees grow bark to protect them from fire and to conserve moisture inside the wood. Splitting firewood accelerates drying and helps it burn better.

If you live in town you won't need to buy commercial firewood at some outrageous price. Your stove will run well on dumpster finds, pallet wood, the waste that your local arborist generates or straight branches, twigs and tree trimmings that can be used in length, gradually feeding themselves into the feed tube.

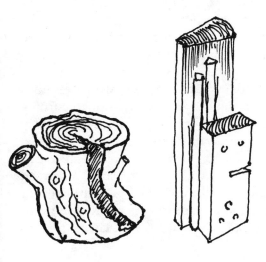

Firewood: the bad and the good.

crooked	straight
short	long
fast grown	slow grown
thick	thin
round	split
thick bark	no bark
knots	fibrous
wet	dry

Choosing Firewood

Cutting your own wood, choose the straightest pieces, sawing close to knots to leave long pieces that are easily split from the not knot end. Trim branch stubs down flush.

Commercial firewood is normally sold by the cord (a stack 4' x 4' x 8'), yet the energy in it is proportional to its weight, not its volume. So try to buy dense firewood. Heavy hardwoods like oak put out nearly twice as much heat per cord as lightweight species such as cottonwood or pine. In a stove with a relatively small feed tube, heavier wood such as oak, ash, beech, birch, madrone or hickory cuts down on how often you need to feed it. Avoid cottonwood, poplar, spruce, hemlock, fir (except Douglas fir), redwood, most pines and cedar (except for kindling).

Because Rocket Stoves work by gravity feed, the wood needs to be fairly straight so it falls into the feed tube without bumps or side branches which might hook it up. Theoretically, a really straight smooth piece of wood can be quite long and should feed itself into the stove automatically, but in practical terms, it's not advisable to use wood much longer than the container around the feed tube or the small barrel containing it. It may burn vertically upwards and fall over, creating a fire hazard or smoke source in the house. Worse, if fuel projects out of the top of an unenclosed feed tube, it can ignite *outside* the tube, flaming up and potentially

reversing the fire's flow. At best, you could be smoked out, at worst, it could set your house on fire.

Here are some situations to avoid: a) Two or more pieces projecting can create a chimney between them, up which the fire can creep against the incoming air. Of special concern would be two pieces of split wood or boards with flat faces facing each other. Even inside the feed tube, try to avoid feeding with flat faces opposing. b) In pocket rockets, a metal stack can get hot enough to ignite fuel sticking out the feed tube several inches away. In each case, problems can be avoided by *keeping the fuel length shorter than the feed tube* and keeping the lid of the small barrel always on top of that barrel, leaving an air crack if needed, but preventing any back burning.

Kiko Denzer points out that his Rocket will cheerfully burn small diameter wood that doesn't even interest his neighbors with their box stoves. Plantation thinnings and straight branches are sometimes just the right size without any splitting, and they're light enough you can enroll your kids into collecting them.

Woods which are excessively resinous such as pitch pine have trouble burning completely and give off unburnable smoke, which tends to condense inside the flue, clogging it up. Avoid woods impregnated with pitch or with creosote, such as railroad ties. You should also **avoid pressure-treated lumber, and wood that is painted, both of** which can contain dangerous chemicals.

Danger of falling out.

Stuck.

Feed the thick end down.

Maintenance

This is not a maintenance-free stove. The Rocket is a non-standardized experimental and whimsical device, which you will probably build for yourself. Each one has a distinct personality that demands regular attention, monitoring and maintenance. There are a few things you should check on quite regularly. Maintenance revolves mostly around keeping all of the tubes clean, a little like the way eating a high fiber diet will clean out your intestines.

Clean the ash out of the combustion chamber regularly. If you ritualize cleaning it every Sunday morning, for instance, you are much less likely to forget. If you don't, it may gradually clog the throat of the heat riser or, worse, ride on through the system and block another tube which is less easy to clean out. Use something hooked like a potato masher or a kitchen ladle to pull ash out of the burn tunnel, then scoop it out of the feed tube with a cup. Or, after making sure the system is really cool, employ a shop vacuum. First, push your hand down into the ashes to make sure they are cool enough to extract. If you can't keep your hands in them, you could have a dangerous situation. Once, for instance, loading warm ash into a plastic bucket, we ran to the phone, leaving the bucket to melt and the hot ash (containing live coals) to spill out onto a wooden floor. Thankfully, the phone caller had the wrong number or our number could have been up. Take ashes (cooled down) back to the woods where they originally came from.

Inspect the horizontal flue in your heat storage every month or two by opening the clean-out and putting in a small mirror and a flashlight. If ash or soot is building up in the pipe, it can be cleaned by either using a vacuum cleaner or pushing a chimney brush through the system. Not having either, I use a long flexible bamboo cane, freshly cut, with twigs and leaves still attached. If you use other vegetation, choose something very fibrous and flexible—you don't want it to break inside the duct. Metal pipes are fitted one into the other with the male end facing upstream, so it may be easier to rod out the system towards the stove, not away from it. If you use a cloth attached to flexible pipe as a flue cleaner, make sure that cloth can't fall off inside the flue. You may have real problems getting it out. Clean the vertical stack at least twice each burning season to remove soot and creosote unless you get little result, in which case, once.

I keep a chimney thermometer in my exhaust stack inside the building where I can see it, just above where the pipe emerges from my heated bench. I check its temperature regularly. It's a very accurate probe-type thermometer that measures the temperature inside the tube, not the magnetized type that sticks to the surface. Probe thermometers are a little more expensive but they are more durable and less likely to fall off and break. Because you don't expect high temperatures, it only needs to read to between 200 and 300°F.

The thermometer is also useful because the temperature of the flue gases will drop when your stove needs to be stoked. Just by casual glances at my thermometer, I can see when pyrolysis is no longer happening, which means usually that either the fire is down to embers or the wood is hanging up instead of falling in by gravity. Familiarity with the stack temperature will alert you to inconsistencies in combustion, or anything that might be wrong in the system such as a slowly clogging flue. A stove that normally generates 250°F at the exit flue, which can only be cranked up to 200°F could be evidence that for some reason the draft is not working well.

Cooking on the Rocket Stove

Rocket Stoves for cooking, using the same basic principles described in this book, are used worldwide, particularly in places where firewood is scarce and the cooking is done inside, necessitating a smoke-free, highly efficient stove. This book mostly covers stoves to heat people, with a few cooking options. The world wide web contains a lot of information on Rocket Stoves including lively and timely discussions, research findings and instructions on how to build a number of different designs. Simply feed the string "Rocket Stove" into your favorite search engine.

Photo: Flemming Abrahamsson

Tiny Rocket Stove for making coffee in Flemming Abrahamsson's office (see section drawing, page 75).

Once you have a functioning stove in your house, you'll probably find unexpected uses for it. Calleagh Ferrara gave birth to her baby on their new Rocket fired cob bench (see Case Studies, page 80).

You can use the top of the barrel as a food dryer, using the gentle residual heat after the fire dies down. It's easy to dry things like seeds and sliced vegetables overnight this way. And of course, there's cooking.

If your choice is to have primarily a cooking stove, there's a compromise. More heat to the cooking surface means less to other places, and when you're *not* cooking that extra heat will chiefly heat the space *above* the stove at a loss of radiant heat from the sides and of stored heat in the thermal battery. Otherwise, if you need chiefly a heating stove, the top of the barrel will be most suitable for simmering or keeping things warm. Now you have a slow cooker for beans or soups, or possibly for toasting nuts, seeds, or foods sliced thinly.

It's also possible to get something boiling on the gas stove, and then put it on the Rocket where it maintains temperature without a vigorous boil. This way you don't lose volatile oils, and you maintain more flavor and enzymes while saving fossil fuels. My own Rocket Stove is not so good at delivering a fast cup of tea in the morning, or for frying, where you need a much higher temperature, but it makes the best toast I've ever tasted.

If you keep a teakettle with a quart or so of water in it on top of your stove, you'll have a source of very hot water. Even when it's not boiling, it will be pre-heated and much faster to bring to a boil on a gas or electric cooker.

With larger Rocket Stoves—a 30-gallon barrel or bigger—a removable stove top oven can be used for baking. The best trick I know is to buy a $1.99 roll of lightweight aluminum kitchen foil and carefully wrap it around to form a little beehive with several thicknesses of foil, shiny face in, to reflect the radiant heat inwards. Tuck the end of the roll over the edge and crimp it together with your hand, then crimp a loose handle at the top. You have an instant oven that will bake good bread, but be sure to support the bottom of the loaf above the barrel top so it doesn't burn. When not in use the oven can be hung up indoors or outside.

In September/October when there's still a lot of surplus fruit and vegetables available, yet the humidity is up especially at night and the temperatures are dropping, we use our Rocket as both house heater and food dryer. You could set up a multi-rack food dryer with stacked screens that sits on top of the barrel.

Tinker around. Any burning or cooking device needs practice. Can you remember the first time you tried to cook on gas or electricity or a pump-up camping stove? It took time to learn to operate the new machine. So play with your stove a lot. Try improbable things and see what happens. Experiment and let us know the results. You may discover something completely new that nobody had ever thought of. If you do, we'll put it in the next edition of this book.

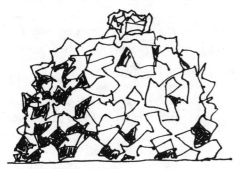

Aluminum foil stovetop oven

Fire! Fire!

★ Don't leave anything in a place where it could possibly fall onto the top of the heat riser barrel or the feed tube. Overhead shelves, wet clothes, towels, kindling, anything plastic or wax or wood or paper. These could all start a fire when you're not looking or produce toxic gas while you're asleep.

★ In stormy weather make sure the gases can't back up through the feed tube. Stop stoking the stove a couple of hours before you go to sleep; make sure the coals are all dead, then put the lid onto the feed as tight as possible.

★ If you're burning long fuel, don't leave it unattended. It may snag up and fail to feed by gravity, then it can burn up to the top of the feed tube and fall over because it's top heavy. Leave a good wide space around the stove without carpet, paper, or anything that could catch fire, and make sure that long pieces of wood burn down before you leave.

★ If you have a tall stack, or a very long horizontal flue, be sure all the joints are air-tight so combustion gases can't seep out into your house. Under no condition should you install a chimney damper; it will constitute a bottleneck that could back up toxic gases such as carbon monoxide.

★ Don't let any smoke get into your living spaces. Even tiny amounts are bad for you. If the stove ever smokes, open all the doors and windows. Don't repeat whatever it was that caused it.

★ Anything hot close to wood can be a problem. If you build above a wooden floor, leave at least a three-inch air gap under the whole combustion unit, glue aluminum foil down on top of the floor and use a minimum of four inches of mineral insulation under the stove and the whole of the heat storage. Over time, heat can build up at the bottom of the heat storage to a high temperature. Similarly, keep a gap from any wood in the walls, remembering that sheetrock-gypsum board nearly always has wood behind it.

★ Firewood needs to be dry, as dry as possible. Wet wood burns badly and gives off water vapor, which may condense to leave creosote somewhere in your system.

★ Design for a long run of duct through the heat storage. More than twenty feet total, if possible. Short runs of duct are not able to absorb as much heat as you would wish. Your exit temperature could be dangerously high.

★ If you employ metal parts that are painted or galvanized in the combustion unit, burn off the paint before installation, out of doors, and remember the fumes can be deadly.

★ Be careful where you burn a Pocket Rocket, they can get extremely hot. Even a five gallon model can radiate at such a high temperature that it can ignite paper several feet away. Site an indoor Pocket Rocket very carefully. Protect children from the metal surface, which can reach over 1000°F.

Burning Questions

Will Rocket Stoves heat every kind of building? They are much more suitable for some uses than others. Keep in mind the trade-offs and limitations.

Heating by these stoves is characterized by quite a lot of convection, a major amount of conduction, but very little useful radiation, except from the top of the heat exchange barrel. The release of heat from storage is slow and gentle over many hours but the stove needs regular attention while it burns.

Compared with a fireplace, which heats you only by radiation and only while it burns, or a metal box stove, which radiates heat from the sides and top but is too hot for conductive comfort, **this is a cuddle-up device.** You can stay warm by being in contact with the storage mass for hours after the fire has died.

The issue is not whether it will heat a building. The building couldn't care less. The issue is whether any heating device provides comfort to the people.

If you live in a big, leaky or uninsulated house, convected heat may be lost before it reaches you. Consider how to get more radiation, less convection and fast response, something you can stand in front of to warm up. You'll use a lot more fuel but that's the price of a house that's big, uninsulated, or leaky. Consider a big Pocket Rocket (see Other Kinds of Rocket) or another type of high radiation stove, with an insulant lid on it, or an efficient wood burning stove.

Rocket Stoves need fairly regular attention and stoking and are better suited to someone who is normally home several hours a day. They are particularly useful if contact heat is arranged (e.g. through the seat for your desk, or where you do phone work or handcrafts or read). And of course, if firewood is expensive and you are trying to put out less greenhouse gas —which is what we all need to do anyway.

Where would I choose not to build a Rocket Stove? Buildings that are irregularly occupied such as churches, meeting halls, etc need to be heated rapidly and don't benefit from long-term stored heat. In large houses with many rooms in very cold zones where heat needs to reach rooms distant from the stove, it might make sense to heat selected rooms by forced hot air. In a work space such as a carpentry shop where one seldom sits down it might be better to have a stove which delivers a lot of radiant heat in place of storing heat, so that you can quickly adjust your comfort by moving closer or further from the stove. In outdoor rooms or living spaces that are not well sealed such as teepees, tents, etc the air heated by the storage would leave the building before you got a chance to enjoy it. Better maybe to put in a stove that delivers high temperature radiation such as a barrel stove or a Rumford fireplace.

Can I run duct work through the floor or interior walls? Almost certainly, unless you already have a poured concrete or a wooden floor. Even in the chilly British Isles, the Romans two thousand years ago heated their villas by hypocausts. A hypocaust is a series of under floor ducts carrying hot gases from a stove. The Romans used sandstone slabs for flooring, set up on stone pillars above a heated crawl space two or three feet high. Today, it might be more convenient to use metal pipes cast into the earthen material or concrete of a floor or laid in sand under brick, tile or flagstone. Remember to put in adequate provision for cleaning out ash or soot, and guard against entry by rodents.

How often do I need to feed it? Fairly often; dragons like to snack regularly. It's one of the delights of the Rocket (for those who enjoy fiddling with a fire). Normally my six-inch diameter system needs attention every 40 minutes to an hour, burning lightweight wood such as alder or maple, but with ash or oak it will happily run a couple of hours without stoking. My 8-inch system needs to be fed every hour to hour-and-a-half on Douglas fir or alder, yet with long, thick pieces of oak, I can sometimes leave it for 3 hours.

Can I leave it to burn all night? It's almost impossible to burn any wood stove all night cleanly. The box wood stoves where you throw in a log and close down the air supply pyrolyze the wood, that is, bake the chemicals out of it. So it smolders all night, generating air pollution. Most of the problems with air pollution from wood stoves come from nighttime smoldering. By contrast, Rockets work well at burning wood fast and clean, and depend upon separate heat storage to keep your house snug. Before you turn in for the night, you let the fire burn out and seal the air supply, then light the stove again the following day.

How long does a cob bench maintain heat? Cushions on the bench will insulate it well. When I rise in the morning I first fold back the bench cushions to allow the thermal battery to warm up the room. Just doing this I sometimes see the room temperature rise 2 to 4 degrees, even after 18–24 hours since the last fire. If I keep the cushions on the bench, it's still warm enough to be comfy a day later. Bigger thermal batteries, such as our Rocket-fired double bed, stay snug two or even three days after a lengthy burn.

How long does the barrel last? Does it burn out? I've never seen one burn out, though we haven't run the same one for more than twelve years. But with all the oxygen used up, so long as you keep it dry, it can't burn from inside nor rust from outside, so it should last a very long time.

But I only have short chunks of firewood. They'll burn fine, but you may need to stoke more often, and the feed tube needs to be quite smooth so they can't jam together and hang up. You will still need long kindling for lighting.

Does it need a direct outdoor air supply? Won't the stove use all the oxygen in my house? Any stove burns oxygen. But it doesn't selectively extract oxygen from your house, leaving you gasping in a room full of nitrogen. It sucks *air* out of the house, not just oxygen. And no, you won't be airless, because as air is sucked down the feed tube, the slight vacuum created in the room pulls in "replacement air" from elsewhere. In very cold climates or very leaky houses this results in drafts, usually from around the bottoms of doors and windows. A separate air vent serving the stove can cut down on these drafts.

How big? A 4-inch pipe should be very adequate. Cover both ends with ¼" metal mesh to keep animals out. Best place? In the ceiling or wall directly above the feed. In mild climates, provided your doors are well-sealed, it may be sufficient to draw cold air down from upstairs, from the many small cracks in a building, through ceiling vents from an attic, etc.

I have read that wood stoves are out-of-date, messy, and a big source of pollution and greenhouse gases. What is the best choice for the environment? While these claims are generally true, woodstoves have been much improved over the past few years, giving off very low emissions and burning efficiently. But there is still a great deal of heat wasted with the conventional wood burning stove. That's why we invented one that is up-to-date, doesn't drop ash on your floor and is extremely efficient. For home comfort, passive solar should definitely be everyone's heating choice. But you may have an existing house that is not solar and can't easily be modified. And, most of us live in places where at least some back-up heat is necessary, or we may want a hot seat to warm up on. Most other heating options are quite literally terminal for our descendants: oil, gas, electric, (from oil, gas, or nuke), or terminal for other species (e.g. dams on salmon rivers). Wood fuel comes from sunlight and replenishes itself every few years as it grows, reabsorbing the carbon dioxide that your stove gives off.

How can I make the old barrels not look like old barrels? You can surround the barrel or cover it partially with sculptural cob or welded artwork. There may be less toxic stove paints with which you could paint it a cheerful color or you could polish it with sand paper or buff it with a wire brush head on an electric drill. Alternatives to barrels include a cylindrical water tank, or a custom built brick column, which is common in Denmark. European mass stoves are usually covered with decorative glazed tiles.

How soon after building it can I fire up my stove? The best way to get it dry is to put a slow fire in it and gradually heat it up. The beauty of working with a lot of sand in a sand-clay mix is that the sand stabilizes the mix and prevents cracking, so you don't have to wait a long time, just dry it gently.

Won't my kids burn themselves? Probably not. We don't have a single report of a child being burned. At baby height the barrel temperature is quite low—perhaps 200–300°F, much cooler than most metal box stoves. Fuel can't roll out and no coals are exposed, as they are in an open fireplace.

How much time should I allow for construction? What takes the most time is preparations—assembling and organizing materials and tools, designing the stove. When everything is ready, two people can easily build a good stove in a weekend, or in a day with practice. The thermal storage might take longer to complete, depending on the size.

My Rocket Stove oscillates, that is it draws fine for a moment, then the draw reverses slightly as if it's changing direction, then it goes back to drawing correctly again, then chugs and sends smoke into the room again. What is the remedy? Blockage (downstream of the heat riser) in the system is the cause of oscillation. The faster it oscillates, the bigger the blockage. Give the whole thing a good cleaning.

Since the heat riser is doing the work of the chimney, can I let the exhaust pipe exit the building low, remaining horizontal, similar to a dryer vent? Try it and see. It won't always work. If it doesn't work, add a section of vertical stack.

How can I improve my stove's draw? Most importantly, make the heat riser taller and insulate it. Clean out the combustion area and all horizontal ducts. Make sure your firewood's dry. Try to use even dryer firewood. Burn thinner firewood.

Are Rocket Stoves code approved? This stove is different from the burning devices that the fire codes are written for; the Rocket's exit flue is considerably cooler than conventional ones, for example, so concerns about materials used in exit tubes may not apply.

Before installing your stove you should know your local code for wood burning devices. Though you may not follow it to the letter for this type of stove, nor intend to inform the building department, codes sometimes help us make wiser choices. What's important is that you do everything safely. Far more significant than issues of legalities are issues of fire safety and preventing toxic gases in your house. In some areas, this stove may present difficulties with the fire department, as it is not certified.

Remember also, that these stoves have not been in regular use for long enough to determine the real risk of chimney fires, so inspect your chimney often.

But what if you're a renter? I am, and there are Rockets in several buildings I rent. You'll have to practice talking nice to the landlord. Prepare some snappy photos of gorgeous looking sculptural Rocket Stove bench assemblies and talk to your landlords demonstrating that you can increase the value of their house. You could show or give to the landlord a copy of this book. They may go for it. Our landlord graciously conceded provided that we agreed to demolish our stove when we leave and replace it with the same space-consuming black box wood burner that was there before.

If your rented house has a wooden floor and/or walls, you will need to take appropriate precautions not to burn it down. In the house that contains our office, where we have a three-ton double bed Rocket heated cob bench, the combustion assembly is raised above the floor about 6 inches with clear space underneath it and insulation is built into the base of the entire stove. We reinforced the floor joists with a stout post in the crawl space beneath the stove. To protect a wall of stud construction or any other burnable material, install at least two inches of high temperature insulation between the wall and the storage bench. Keep the combustion unit at least a foot and-a-half from the wall with an air space in between and face the wall with aluminum foil, shiny side towards the stove. To help reduce temperatures at the wall you could also install a fresh air intake pipe between stove and wall as a cooler. This will also prevent the stove from sucking all the warm air out of your house.

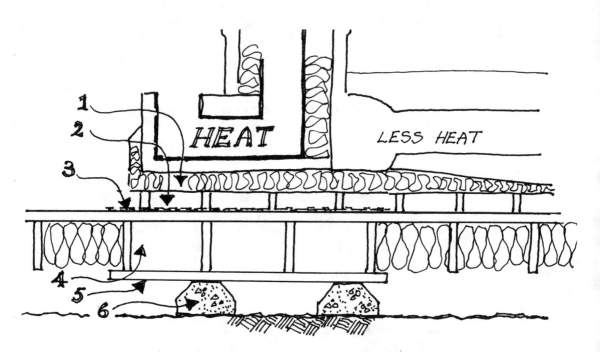

Eight-inch Rocket Stove built over a wooden suspended floor.
1. Four-inch mineral-clay insulation, suspended on four-inch brick edge.
2. Four-inch air-flow space.
3. Two layers of crumpled aluminum foil glued to floor surface, shiny side up.
4. Floor insulation removed below combustion unit.
5. Two-inch board for reinforcement.
6. Twelve-inch concrete pier blocks wedged in tight.

Burn tunnel length equal to heat riser height.

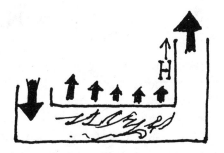

Burn tunnel length is twice that of the heat riser. Half the draft; twice the heat loss from the burn tunnel.

Relative proportions of burn tunnel, heat riser and feed tube.

Heat riser is twice the height of the burn tunnel length: Ideal. Twice the draft.

Feed tube too high. Burn-back can happen with poor draft. Heat riser is effectively shorter.

Trouble Shooting

Stove smokes into the house. There is probably a bottleneck somewhere in the system. Here are some possibilities:

• First, check if you need to **clean ash out** of the burn tunnel. Occasionally something will fall down the heat riser such as mortar from between the bricks.

• Perhaps some wet mud fell into the tube as you sealed the last hole.

• Experimental liners for the heat riser may break up and fall inwards. An example was the ceramic tile drains we tried out in the early days. They can't take the thermal shock so they tend to explode, showering shrapnel down the hole. So **clean out the burn tunnel** very thoroughly all the way to the end.

• If the **feed tube was built too wide**, it has the same effect. You can test by sliding a loose brick or wood block across the top of the feed tube. If all smoking stops when for instance you have it one-third covered, provided there's still a good draft you could make the brick permanent.

• More than once, I've been phoned by someone who, on investigation, found they had residual **unburned newspaper** in the primer hole.

• Once, a dead wood rat was sadly mummified in the tunnel of my heated bench. Another time, following a summer of inactivity, there was a **mouse nest** clogging the exhaust pipe. A piece of ¼" wire mesh over the end of the flue will prevent animals climbing in.

• Unburned carbon can be deposited and can accumulate slowly, gradually building up like black hoarfrost inside the pipes, especially if you burn pitchy wood or conifer bark. Clean it out from time to time.

• The bench was **built with a bottleneck** in it. Perhaps there were too many right angle bends, or a flimsy metal pipe collapsed during construction.

• The space at the top of the heat riser could be too tight; a noticeable hot spot right over the heat riser could be a clue.

• If smoke gradually develops over days or weeks, there could be a build-up of ash somewhere else, probably where the gases exit from the combustion unit into the heat storage. Any obstructions in the stack are

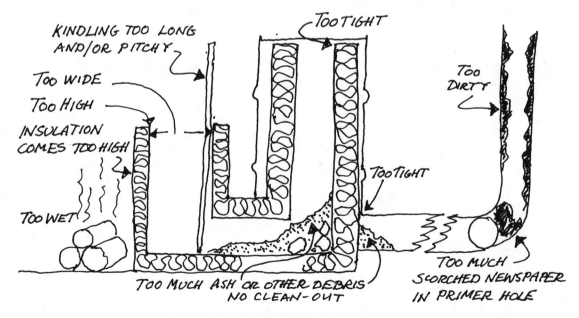

Looking for trouble? Try these places.

at risk of backing up toxic gases, especially carbon monoxide and oxides of nitrogen.

Because the combustion unit is **pushing** cool gases up the stack, whereas with box stoves the hot stack gas itself is pulling gas upwards, be extra careful to ensure there are no obstructions in the exit stack. For instance, a spark arrester on the exit could block with soot, unnoticed, or possibly unburned paper from the primer hole could fly up the stack and lodge there. In either case there's a chance of toxic gases such as carbon monoxide backing up and escaping into the house.

• Sometimes, using **long pitchy kindling** will cause the burn to rise up the feed tube. Fire will seek out the easily flammable dry pitch and creep vertically up the wood towards the top of the wood, sometimes burning outside the feed tube. If you use pitchy wood, keep it shorter than the feed tube. If the fire still burns up the hole, fill the entire feed tube with fuel, constricting the ability of the stove to burn backwards up the fuel. Keep a brick handy to cover part of the feed tube opening if there's a persistent problem, or if the small barrel has a lid, experiment with how far closed it needs to be. If it persists in being naughty, the time-tested remedy of a good shaking is likely to improve things.

• The first time you light your new stove, don't expect immediate success. Don't be downhearted if it smokes like crazy and it's hard to get a draw. With any new masonry stove which is still cold and wet when you first fire it, there will be an adjustment period. Use the primer, fire it up with the driest, thinnest wood you have and be patient. It may take several hours for it to start burning really well.

I can't get a quick boil. This means the temperature of the top of the barrel just isn't high enough. Good tea is worth waiting for, but if the problem is a cool cooking surface, it may be that the top of the barrel is too far from the top of the heat riser.

The heat produced is being scattered across the whole surface. You may want to **bring them closer together** to concentrate heat in the center.

For fast cooking, **stoke with thin split wood,** it will burn faster. We've seen Rocket cook stoves get hot enough in the center to glow orange.

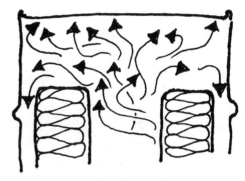

Equal heat all over.

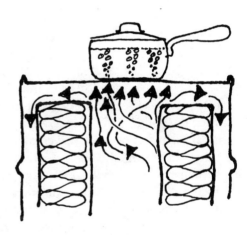

Heat concentrated in center.

When cooking or boiling water, some simple things to remember include:

• Burn dry wood.

• Cast iron or any heavy cookware heats up slowly; stainless steel loses heat slowly.

• Don't put in more water than you immediately need.

• Always **put a lid on** the pot, it can make a huge difference in how long it takes to boil.

• If the pot tends to be sluggish, try laying an insulated, non-flammable pot holder on top of the lid.

•The bigger the surface area of the bottom of the pot, the faster heat can get to it. Tall, narrow teakettles take a long time to boil; use a short, wide pot.

•You could be making tea in an unaccustomed high altitude location, where although the water boils at a lower temperature, there's less oxygen in the air, so the fuel doesn't burn as hot.

Condensation in the exhaust pipe and duct work.
Clean burning of even dry wood produces water vapor, but you probably have enough heat in most parts of your pipes to prevent condensation, at least inside the building. Outdoors, an uninsulated metal exhaust pipe stack will condense liquid water at any time the air temperature is low, particularly if your heat storage is really efficient, lowering the exit temperature of the gases to near condensation point. Condensates may be pure water or may contain some creosote. A newly constructed stove takes days to dry out so don't despair if there's a lot of condensate during that time.

However if you experience ongoing condensation in the tubes that are inside your house, there's something seriously wrong. A possible cause is that condensation created **outside** is able to flow down the pipe passing through the wall. The pipe then needs adjustment so that it drops slightly to the outside.

Most likely you are burning wet wood. How can you tell if your firewood is too wet? Easy. Weigh some, straight from the wood stack, split thin as a finger, leave it on the top of the warm stove overnight and weigh it again the next day. If you don't have an accurate scale, you can take a great armful, at least 20 pounds, onto the bathroom scale with you and subtract your own weight. Or if you have only a postal scale, which probably goes to two pounds, use a small sample. You'll get a fairly accurate reading. More than 10 precent weight loss in a night and your firewood was disastrously wet, even 5 percent lost indicates it was too wet to burn cleanly.

Soot/creosote builds up in the exhaust pipe.
Wood may be **lying down** in the burn tunnel. This squeezes the fuel together and deprives it of oxygen while letting cold air flow over the top of it. Stand it up, leaning it against the forward wall of the feed tube, letting it drop-feed by gravity as it burns.

Cracking caused by metal parts in earthen stoves.
Any junction between dissimilar building materials creates stresses. In places where metal parts are in tight contact with cob, brickwork or stone, heating and cooling create cyclic expansion/contraction.

A common example is a steel barrel heat exchanger enclosed or partially buried in cob or sand-clay. If at all possible, try to leave space for that expansion or use flexible material in direct contact with the metal. Our friend Meka has experimented with using perlite-clay to buffer a wood heating stove from the cob walls surrounding it. Another solution is to welcome the cracks, make allowance for them as is done in urban sidewalks by scoring the surface so that cracking occurs in a predictable pattern. Make sure this scoring is superficial and that the mortar is airtight around the barrel so that gases can't escape and suffocate you.

Drawbacks of Rocket Stoves

Nothing's perfect, except, arguably, Nature herself. Human gadgetry always has a downside. In place of extravagant claims—"the wood stove you always wanted" (how do we know what you wanted?) or "This stove will solve all your heating problems" (it almost certainly won't)—we wanted to address aspects of Rocket Stoves that people have found difficult.

Stoking needs to happen quite often, whereas you can fill a big box stove with wet wood and smolder it overnight. With practice, straight, long dense wood and good luck you can feed a 6-inch system every half to three hours, an 8-inch every two to four hours. You can't keep it alight and burning clean all night, so it needs to be lit fresh each day, and in a few cases, twice a day.

Long straight wood works better. What if your firewood supply is all curved, short, knotty, branched? Well, self-feeding by gravity gets difficult, so you might need a different design of feed tube, horizontal perhaps with a grate beneath and a closed door. We need more research from the knotty hardwood zone.

Too much work splitting wood. In practice, a 6-inch system won't take wood thicker than your forearm, an 8-inch system won't take wood bigger than your knee. If you don't enjoy splitting firewood, or if your firewood is difficult to split, burn small roundwood, or design a bigger diameter system. A 10-inch flue can have an 8" x 10" feed tube, and could take wood up to about 7 inches. A 12-inch system (which we haven't tried yet) could probably stand a 10" x 12" feed. Big diameter systems are more suited to big heat storage, long heat extraction tubes and multiple flue pipes, for instance for floor heating.

Key parts need frequent replacement. In the combustion chamber, temperatures are very high (up to 2000°F) and thermal stress is intense. Thermal stress means the rate of temperature change is high. Also the hottest spot constantly moves around as the fuel burns and settles. Steel parts in the feed tube or burn chamber disintegrate by slow combustion and ceramic parts such as brick crack, spall and crumble. The fastest damage is often in the bridge covering the burn tunnel and around the base of the feed tube where the burn tunnel begins. It would be useful to find a more durable material. Perhaps castable ceramic or cast iron would perform better. More research is needed.

Ash clean-out is not always easy. Cross sectional sizes in the combustion area are fairly critical so stove performance suffers from ash buildup. Easier clean-out might solve the procrastination factor. My own process goes like this: (a) As I clean out ash, I tell myself, "Get it out quicker next time!" (b) I burn my stove quite a lot in cold weather. (c) Every few days I remember I need to clean out ash. Each time other priorities get in the way, or I can't be bothered to look for the clean-out tool, or last night's ash is still too hot to handle, or I loaned out my only metal bucket, the one I can safely load with hot ash or it's dark, or it's Thursday, or there's a letter "R" in the month. (d) My stove gets gradually harder to light. I blame everything except ash buildup such as wet wood, bad luck, bad weather, my own incompetence, etc. (e) Stove occasionally smokes into my house. Remedy? Keep the lid on the feed barrel, shake the fuel down more often, anything but empty ash. (f) Finally, I give in, find tool and bucket, kneel on a cushion, empty an almost clogged system. An 8-inch system can yield 2 to 3 gallons of ash. Time taken? About ten minutes, including redistributing ash, cleaning tools. (g) Tell myself, "Get to it quicker next time!"

I think you can see the remedies. First, have a ritual clean-out day, say every Sunday morning before lighting it. If necessary, put it on the calendar. Second, keep the clean-out tools and ash bucket in an easily accessible place. Third, try to remember that most smoking or hard to start problems are caused by an obstruction, usually of ash.

Rocket Stoves need a sophisticated operator. Rocket Stoves are an invitation to be involved. Choice of fuel is an art, both when selecting it and as you feed it piece by piece. Here's a stove that continuously reminds you of the diversity of Nature. If you screw up, fail to pay attention, or work too fast, the stove punishes you with smoke in your house or it's hard to start or too much stoking, splitting or cutting wood. Not a stove for people who rent their house, unless they have real interest in the process. Also not so good for guest houses, hotels, or situations with rapid turn-over of residents. And finally, in just a few cases, they just plain don't work. Of conventional box stoves you could probably say that they *mostly* don't work, so don't be alarmed. We know of only three non-working examples of Rocket Stove. Two were built by neophytes whose symptoms were impossible to diagnose by phone, so perhaps we can discount that. But the third was a demonstration stove built at a workshop. How embarassing! With every adjustment we could conjure up to try, it still won't work well. It backdrafts, filling the whole house with smoke, and we just can't figure out why. Don't let any of this discourage you. There are hundreds of rocket stoves in operation. Most of them without a glitch.

Slow response time. This is another major issue with the rocket mass heater. If the house and bench get cold, it can take a while to heat them up again. In climates where heating needs are intermittent, the system works less efficiently.

The fire is difficult to see. If you're used to the visual magic of armchair fire gazing, you may find it difficult. You can however watch it from above, and there's the compensation of **listening**. Rocket Stoves are an audial feast. Burning strongly, they can roar, in fact like a little rocket, and the intense temperatures snap and crackle the firewood. Subtler is the gentle thud every so often as a piece falls down the feed tube, when you hear the burn respond immediately. We've heard reports that this sound was what people liked best of all. "It's instructive. I can attend it by sound prompts."

Conversely, the thuds and shufflings remind your subconscious that the stove still has fuel. When they stop, you will gradually notice it. As with little kids in another room, it's when they go quiet that you have to check them out. As long as there's noise, everything is okay.

Do you really need to see the fire from your couch? Turn off the lights and watch dancing patterns on the ceiling. You'll rest in peace.

Adaptations & Other Kinds of Rocket

We have given you a very specific recipe for making one particular model of one size of one kind of Rocket Stove with minor variations. This is like a recipe for chocolate chip ginger saffron cookies with 143 grams of butter, 212 grams of flour, 96.7 grams of honey and exactly a quarter of a pinch of salt. In other words, we've tried to faithfully give you the instructions to build one stove which we know works well.

Now you're wondering if there's any flexibility in the measurements, proportions or materials. Already I can hear you asking "But what if...?" "What if I don't have any mason's sand? Or if I can only find 7-inch pipe? What if your stove doesn't fit into my house? What would happen if I wanted the bench higher? Can I heat my walls or floor, or build a stove for a completely different use, such as heating a workshop? Or a teepee? An ice-cream parlor?" When we change one variable, it changes everything else, so you will want to know the significance of changes you may make. As with many aspects of physics, a linear scale-down is not normally followed by the same scale-down in area or volume. A fire twice the size doesn't do everything twice as much as one that is half the size. But we can make some predictions about how well variations will probably work and from experience we can warn you about some things that definitely do not.

Start by consulting Dimentia and Proportia. Almost certainly if you choose to make the heat riser higher the stove will burn faster, whereas if you choose to make the exhaust pipe higher it will have very little effect. If you make the heat riser shorter you will come to a point where it doesn't work at all, but we don't know exactly where. You would just have to try it. The longest heat storage flue we have seen is over 30 feet and it performs excellently, so we can speculate that a 55-gallon barrel with an 8-inch flue can push hot gases 40, 50, probably 60 feet. Beyond that is more speculation.

We also know that heat is lost more rapidly from hot objects than cooler ones. So the most critical part to insulate will be the surroundings of the burn tunnel. The stove we describe in detail heats people in a small house in a fairly mild winter climate quite effectively. For a bigger house or a colder climate (or colder people) you might try to scale up the whole unit, making the entire digestive tract a bigger cross sectional area and making the heat riser taller.

For heating a greenhouse you can run your exhaust pipes through the floor to minimize wasted space and maximize the amount of heat storage placing it as low in the building as possible. But with a greenhouse stove, moisture is always present and you would be advised to build with flues that won't rust, using for instance brick, stainless steel or aluminum.

THE ROCKET HOT TUB

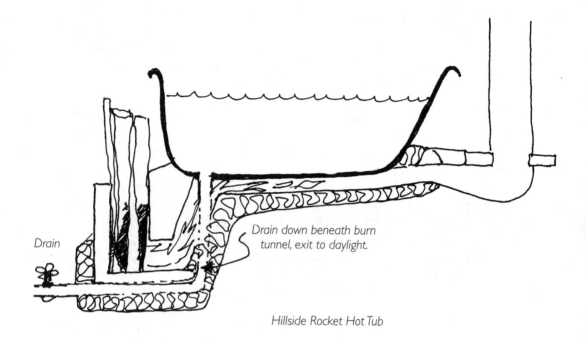

Drain

Drain down beneath burn
tunnel, exit to daylight.

Hillside Rocket Hot Tub

If you have an old cast iron bathtub, you can fairly easily turn it into a one-person makeshift hot tub. It may need to be under a roof to protect the cob parts from rain.

Take an old clawfoot bathtub, twenty or so used bricks, and a few feet of chimney pipe. Dig a trench the length and width of the tub, fairly shallow. A gap 1½" to 2" deep is ideal, the full width of the tub's bottom. Line it with pyro-insulant (we've used a ratio of 1 clay-slip to 6 perlite). Set the tub down carefully over its trench, and seal the sides with insulation. To drain the tub, attach a vertical drainpipe straight down through the insulative trench floor and discharge away from the area, perhaps to thirsty plants downhill of the tub. Dig a pit just in front of the drain end of the tub, a foot deeper than the trench, and construct a brick feed tube in it. Connect the tub to the feed tube with a perlite-clay fire tunnel, lifting the tunnel floor steeply so the hot gases collide with the tub's floor. A few inches from the head end, a brick base holds up the exhaust pipe, which is worth insulating, though that's not essential.

Use a floating bubble-wrap cover or an old closed-cell foam camping pad that fits the tub tightly, or the water as it heats will simultaneously cool by surface heat loss. You will also need a bum-saver, a wooden board to insulate your butt from the hot iron beneath. Always make sure that you have at least ten gallons of water in the tub before firing or you'll crack the enamel. And, don't even try a fiberglass bathtub; the smell as it melts is atrocious.

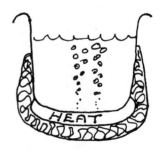

Note wide tunnel and
insulation placement.

Depending on how you rank the distinguishing features of a Rocket Stove, some of the following examples of other kinds of Rocket Stoves could be seen as Something Else. They have some Rocket characteristics, but not all, they lack heat storage, for example. Although they burn extremely clean, they do so at the cost of wasting heat up the stack. We thought it worthwhile to include them though, as they may stimulate further tinkering.

DETROITUS AND THE POCKET ROCKET

Shortly after Larry and Sandy bought their farm, and long before they built the house there, he and I were working all day in the rain. There was no shelter, it was midwinter and we got soaked and chilled. As darkness came on, we packed our tools and drove back to the pickers' shack Larry and Sandy had rented on another place. Just the time for a hot shower and a mug of cocoa in front of a blazing fire!

We had the cocoa, but there was no shower in the shack and no easy way to warm up. California farmers clearly felt little need at that time to provide comfort for their seasonal workers. We were blue with cold; the cocoa didn't help that much. Finally we switched on the gas stove and sat with our feet in the oven. After a while, Larry looked at me and laughed. "This is ironic," he said. "Two of the world's experts on improved stoves sitting with their feet in a gas oven. Why don't we build a wood stove?" So we bundled up and went back out into the pouring rain with a flashlight.

Like many California farms the place was rich with junk piles—"Detroitus" as David Eisenberg calls it.

We found a 55-gallon barrel and assorted lengths of rusty stove pipe and took them back with the vague notion, I suppose, that we could build a barrel stove by banging a door into one end of the barrel, laying it flat and poking a flue into the other end. But somehow we screwed up. The frigidity of the night must have affected our brains. Both holes ended up at the same end of the barrel. So we stood it upright, connected the flue to one hole and poured burning kindling down the other. It took off instantly, roaring loudly. Little did we know we had invented the Pocket Rocket. But then we didn't care much; it was just too comfy, slowly rotating our steaming bodies and sipping hot cocoa.

The stove that Larry Jacobs and I made was an ancestor of Rocket mass heaters. How they work has to do with the fuel and the incoming air both being preheated because the feed tube is actually inside the burn chamber. They are similar in that there is an abrupt 180-degree bend at the bottom of the feed tube, there is gravity feed and the feed chamber is separate from combustion. The high temperature of the combustion chamber and the stack drags in fresh air at high velocity. Pocket Rockets waste a lot of heat up the stack so it's good to use a small diameter pipe but they are incomparable for delivering foot-level radiant heat quickly out-of-doors in even the worst weather.

We later played with the idea at an alternative kid's school in England, scaling it down to as small as a three quart paint can with a bean can for a feed and a 2-inch downspout for the stack. We taught workshops to suburban housewives on how to make a 5-gallon Pocket Rocket with a tire iron and a rock in about 25 minutes if you're stuck at the side of a road near a landfill.

and it can get alarmingly hot. We've had them cherry red all-round and hot enough for the can to buckle up like a concertina: a dangerous source of heat radiation that can ignite flammable objects at 2 and 3 feet distance. Be sure to keep the kindling, paper, furniture, etc. at least three feet away or suround your pocket with a safety wall of brick, cob or polished aluminum.

THE GUATEMALAN COOK STOVE: ESTUFA ROCKY

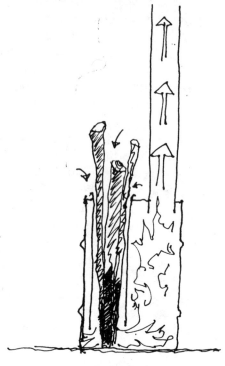

Pocket Rocket

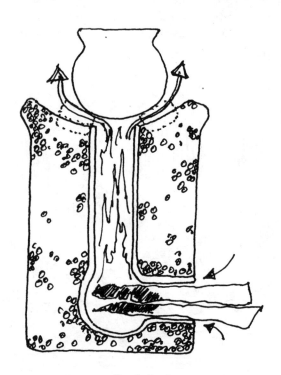

Estufa Rocky

Our dream was that they could be taught to homeless people to get fast heat on windy street corners by burning scrap lumber out of dumpsters.

Recently, Tracy Johnson made a truly Pocket-size one with a beer can and two pieces of 1-inch steel pipe. "Hard to keep it going though," she says.

Note also that the greatest heat output is from the *bottom* of the pocket rocket

In the late '80s my work as a trainer for the Peace Corps caught the attention of the Guatemalan Minister of Agriculture. He thought that a clean burning wood fired cook stove for the urban populations, especially in Guatemala City, could reduce the devastating deforestation happening all around the capital city. At that time more than a million people did their daily cooking on little open campfires inside their homes, particularly the recent settlers in the huge squatments that filled the steep ravines surrounding the more formal parts of town. Daily, huge trucks brought massive loads of pine firewood in from the mountains. It was sold in street markets or in corner stores at a substantial price. Families were spending up to one third of their meager incomes on cooking fuel. For some people the choice was to cook or to buy food; they couldn't afford both. As with anything the government wants, everything had to happen quickly, so suddenly I had a staff of five and a lab in Guatemala City and 12 days to come up with a stove that would cut firewood use in half.

The device we developed cut fuel use by more than 50 percent and was the fastest cooking stove of the hundreds I tested in those years. Its core was a terra-cotta elbow 4 inches in diameter which created a heat riser about 20 inches tall and a horizontal feed tube about 10 inches long. The elbow was cast into a lightweight pumice-concrete cylinder and cooking happened on top of the heat riser. We made no attempt to get the small amounts of smoke it produced out of the house. At a budget of US$4 per stove there was little room for refinements.

The Minister of Agriculture, delighted by the results but a pragmatic realist said, "What do you mean 'Rocket Stove?' That sort of title will never fly in Guatemala. We will call it *Estufa Rocky!*" ("Rocky" was the name of a series of movies which were very popular in Guatemala at the time).

Most of the users loved these stoves. Not so much for their firewood savings, (who counts firewood anyway unless you have a scale and a laboratory?) but because they cook really fast. It is a marvel to people who normally cook on an open fire to be able to keep the fire going with only one stick.

THE BENGALI PIT STOVE

In the heavily populated delta of the Brahmaputra, rural people lack many resources and are desperately short of cooking fuel. Long before Rocket Stoves were around, the people there developed underground stoves using similar principles.

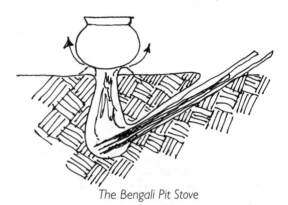

The Bengali Pit Stove

Combustion happens in a flask-shaped pit about a foot-and-a half deep. The fire is fed with tiny pieces of sticks and agricultural waste through a diagonal tunnel, which intersects the bottom of the pit (see diagram). Dry soil is quite a good insulant, so the burn is very hot. The cook pot is suspended on three little clay hills equally spaced around the rim of the pit.

These stoves are extremely efficient in the amount of fuel used and the speed with which they cook, and they have a great advantage over fires or stoves above ground. In a very hot climate, waste heat radiating from a cooking fire can add to the cook's discomfort. Nearly all of the pit stove's heat goes into the pot.

You might try this one next time you go camping, or even in your backyard. The investment is minimal and the rewards are high.

HEATING WATER

A frequent question is "What about heating water?" Nothing conclusive, but we've tried a few things. You might do the same.

Our first attempt was a 60-gallon gas heated water tank (from the dump, for free) mounted atop a 55-gallon standard Rocket. The exit gases roar up the heat riser, then straight through the tube in the center of the tank. The tank is insulated, and the barrel is stuffed with loose perlite all around the brick heat riser.

Things we learned:

1. A three-inch flue is too small; it takes 1½ to 3 hours to get up to shower temperature. At the North American School of Natural Building this works okay because most evenings there is demand for ten to twenty showers and the 60-gallon tank yields about that many if you keep stoking between showers.

2. The whole contraption is very high, about ten feet with the exit stack, seven or so without it.

3. Sixty gallons of water in a steel tank weighs a quarter of a ton. It feels precarious so high up. What could happen if the support barrel tilted, collapsed or rusted through? How would it do in an earthquake, and would you have to run for your life naked and soapy?

4. Loose-fill perlite settles over time, so the top few inches of the barrel are now very poorly insulated.

As part of Cob Cottage Company's ongoing research project, Ernie Wisner is using a coil of twenty feet of half-inch copper tube wrapped around a triple-wall stainless steel stove pipe / heat riser. It feeds into a standard water heater tank. Early results look very promising, though with a bigger pipe, say ¾", you could expect a much faster heat-up.

For instant hot water, a coil of ½" copper pipe in a Pocket Rocket delivers very hot water within minutes. Easy to make, very little fuel, but you need to be there to feed it and to make sure the water stays flowing.

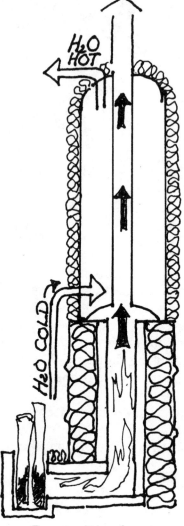

The general idea of a water heater mounted atop the heat riser of a Rocket Stove.

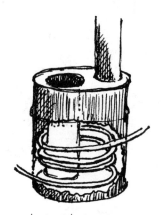

Instant hot water.

THE COFFEE ROCKET

In the office of our Danish partner, Flemming Abrahamsson, among the stylish Scandinavian furniture and beautifully drawn plans on his desk sits a little thermal fiberboard box recessed into the surface of the desk (see photo, page 56). When clients come to discuss the architecture of their buildings, Flemming asks, "Would you like some coffee?" He puts the coffee pot on top of the box and sticks a match in its mouth. His Coffee Rocket boils a liter of water in four minutes, easily outdoing gas or electricity and produces so little smoke that it has no need for a chimney. It's made of low-density, high-temperature mineral fiberboard, which you can buy by the sheet and cut with a handsaw.

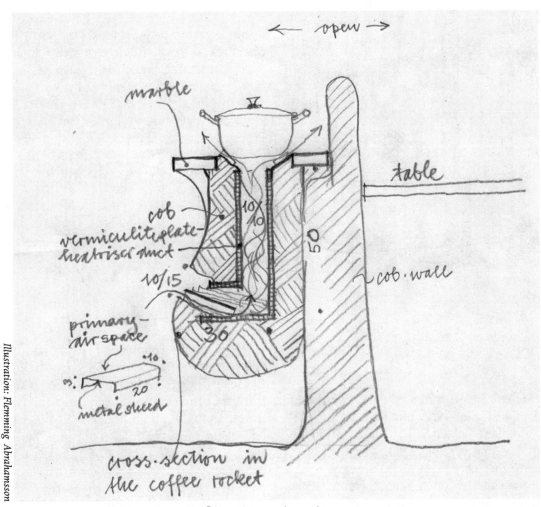

Illustration: Flemming Abrahamsson

Dimensions are in centimeters.

HOW TO MAKE A POCKET ROCKET

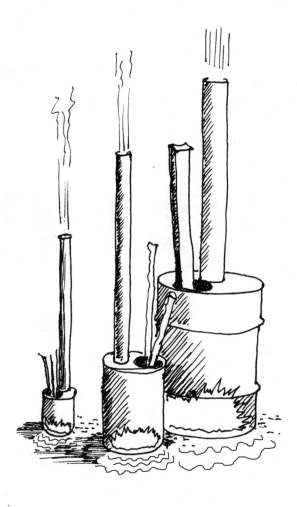

This recipe is for a Pocket Rocket with a five-gallon burn chamber (using a 5 gallon can or pail). It's possible to make one in any size. The pipe sizes will be proportional. For example, a 25-gallon drum works well with an 8" x 25" feed tube, and a 4" x 66" flue pipe. These measurements are fudge-able. It's the proportions that matter.

MATERIALS:

5-gallon metal can or pail with removable lid, clean of finish paint or residue

4 inch x 60 inch pipe (preferably not galvanized)

6 inch x 12 inch pipe (not galvanized, flat black stove pipe is preferred for both)

Sheet metal scrap of at least 4 inch x 4 inch (or something similar: steel pie pan, vegetable strainer, steel pot lid, etc)

Newspaper

Firewood: dry, thin, straight, long

Plenty of tiny kindling

TOOLS:

tin snips

hammer and nail

hole saw

pliers

felt-tip marker

SAFETY GEAR:

leather gloves

Pocket Rockets come in many shapes, sizes and styles. The type pictured is an outdoor radiant heater. It's made from cheap materials that are often found in the waste stream. Because of its high chimney, it has a relatively clean burn, but of course what heat isn't absorbed by a human directly off the radiant barrel is sent to the heavens. The emissions are low, though, making it a nice way to get warm around a fire in the city, for example. It requires very little wood to operate. It is also easy to make.

Remove the residues of paint and the pail's contents (see a note on safety, below). Remove the rubber gasket, if there is one, from the inside of the lid. The feed tube and the flue pipe are both attached at the same end of the burn chamber (the can or pail) in the lid. Trace the outline of the two pipes onto the lid with a felt marker (or nail, etc), placing each pipe towards the outer rim of the lid so that there will be plenty of material left in the lid itself to support the pipes (see illustration, following page). In order to create a tight fit for the pipes, draw a circle that is an inch all-around smaller inside the original one.

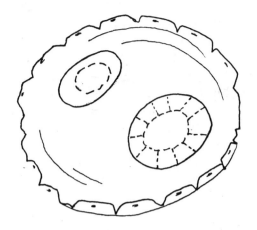

The flip-side of a can lid with large and small pipes traced onto it.

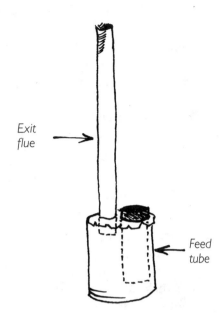

Exit flue

Feed tube

Start the hole in the center with a hammer and nail, chisel or other sharp object. Then from the starter hole, use tinsnips to cut out the inner hole. An easy way to do this is to cut in a spiral pattern from the center out to the inner marker line. Do the same for the other pipe. Now you have a can lid with two holes which are both too small to accomodate the pipes. Using tinsnips, cut tabs about an inch wide, radially from the hole's center out to the pipe's actual line. These tabs will hold the pipes in firm and tight and allow much more control and adjustment when fitting them. Using pliers, fold the tabs almost to right angles pointing into the can. Now you have a dangerous frisbee.

Can lid with tabs cut out and folded back.

The shorter, bigger pipe, which is the feed tube, will hang inside the can, almost to the bottom (see illustration). The long exit flue pipe will sit into the can only a few inches, just enough to hold it steady. Put the lid on the can and friction-fit the two pipes into position, making adjustments to the tabs as necessary so that there is a nice tight fit.

Operation Light the corner of a piece of crumpled newspaper and push it down the feed under the area of the flue. Flames should be drawing up the flue pipe. Slowly feed more burning newspaper to burn at the bottom of the feed tube. Add a little more newspaper then a few pieces of kindling, standing upright in the feed hole. The object is to keep the draft going in the same direction: into the flue. Add more fuel. You can regulate airflow into the stove with a piece of sheet metal a little larger than the pipe. There are many ways to enhance the burn quality. Experiment!

A note on safety. A lot of the pipe out there is galvanized. Its melting point is 787°F, but it offgases at a lower temperature than that. We like to just avoid galvanized pipe.

Most barrels are painted. This paint must be burned off in a bonfire to remove it. Who is downwind (including you)? Wear robust leather gloves, and stay out of the smoke.

Research Needed and Experiments

In the year and a half since the first edition was published, considerable experimental work has been done. All by amateurs, some of it with surprising results. We now know more about geometric relationships, proportion and ways to heat water, for example. But as with any good research, more questions than answers are generated. This remains an exciting field, wide open for low-cost research by anyone with a little time and creativity. Cob Cottage Company will continue to be a clearing house for new information and will happily put researchers in touch with one another.

Experiments with **bigger stoves** with **bigger power outputs** might be interesting. So far, most Rocket Stoves have been built with 6-inch or 8-inch diameter exhaust pipes. They might necessitate more durable, high-temperature materials, such as castable ceramic, fireclay-fiber mixes, or fireclay-insulant mixes for the combustion zone.

How far horizontally can a Rocket Stove push hot gases? Our own greenhouse stove works well with 36 feet of exhaust flue and no vertical stack. What would it take to heat sixty or a hundred feet?

Less work in splitting firewood and less frequent attention are desirable. Ways of creating a bigger feed chamber would help a lot.

A submersible Rocket Stove for heating hot tubs? In the 1980's, an enterprising inventor in a physics laboratory at the University of Alaska came up with a welded aluminum wood stove called the Snorkel, specifically designed to heat a wooden hot tub. It had some similarities to the Rocket but the fire chamber was not separated from heat storage so the combustion temperature was too low for a clean burn. Someone inventive should be able to improve on that.

Saunas and sweat lodges could well be Rocket powered. There is a lot of interest in this.

What about a Rocket with the fuel loaded vertically in a closed loading stack, with the **air inlet on the side at the bottom** of the feed tube? It might be that you could expose the air vent as a very small window of very hot fire visible in the room, heating the feet by direct radiation. For chunky or curved fuel, would a horizontal loader be worthwhile? What disadvantages would it have?

Castable pre-assembled kits would make building these stoves more accessible to more people.

A foolproof self-loader to guide fuel into the feed-tube could help with the use of longer wood or very short wood such as wood chips, pellets or sawdust, and should protect from burning pieces falling out of the stove.

The basic Snorkel concept.

Increased durability of key components. In particular, the bottom of the feed tube and the bridge over the burn tunnel.

Home-made fireproof insulants, e.g. clay-sawdust, clay-wood chips, clay-paper fiber, etc.

Better Pocket Rockets. More durable feed pipe, safer surfaces, less stack heat loss, their use as cookstoves. All are promising, as is a wider range of applications. For instance can a Pocket Rocket be a mass heater? Or, how could we store the heat produced?

How about a Rocket Stove that runs on **clean construction waste and forest thinnings?** If your access to burnable fuel is from forest restoration thinnings, or from the cut-offs from carpentry projects, what would your Rocket Stove look like? We'll be working at this one over the next year, as many people find themselves in this position, wishing to cut down on flammable materials in their forests, or wishing to rescue fuel from the waste stream.

Hypocausts means underfloor heating by hot gas. They were used 2000 years ago in the chilly British Isles by the Romans. Normally they used sandstone slabs for the floor, suspended on sandstone pillars about three feet high. Now that underfloor "radiant" (hot water or electrical) heating is popular, this may be something useful to explore.

An underfloor Rocket Stove for melting aluminum. Shannon Dealy is currently finishing up and testing an aluminum forge in his cob workshop. Firewood is fed horizontally into an outdoor feed tube. The burn tunnel passes through the cob wall, and the heat riser is two barrels stacked and welded end-to-end to create enough draw for the temperature required to melt aluminum (1200°F). Four manifolds, made from square steel tubing, guide the cooling gases through under-floor pipes in the shop, making it so

warm in there that when Shannon fired it up to dry the floor, it did more than dry, it drove him out!

Beehive ovens normally bake really well, but burn really dirty. Shortage of oxygen and low surround temperature, coupled with no effective chimney, are a bad combination for clean burning. A little experimental work by Jim and Tyra Arraj hints at possibilities for a better bread oven with cleaner burn, greater efficiency, and fewer neighbors calling out the fire truck.

The Arrajes installed a short removable chimney, which creates suction that hurtles pre-heated air down the down-draft pipe onto the fuel. The oven door is kept closed except when adding fuel.

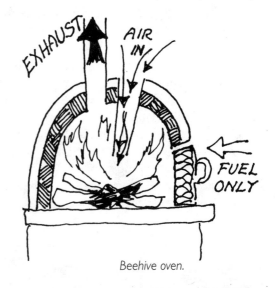

Beehive oven.

Case Studies

TOM & CALLEAGH *live in a cob house they built at a community in the mountains of Northern California. Their home is extremely remote. In winter, it's an 8-mile hike with a four thousand foot climb to the nearest drivable road.*

After building the cob house and living in it for a year or two, we'd both had plenty of time to think about a central heat source for the house. The idea for a mass heater bench came up, but I had doubts about building a mass heater that would actually work. My mind always came back to the tried and true 'airtight wood stove' option: compact efficient and familiar—or so I thought!

In February 2002, we participated in the Pyromania workshop with Cob Cottage Company. There we learned about cob fireplaces and construction, but most importantly for us, we experienced for the first time sitting on a warm, cozy and very functional wood fired mass heater bench—three of them, in fact! After this experience, I immediately threw the airtight wood stove idea out the window. 'Air-tight?' Wood stoves are anything but efficient. Convenient, perhaps. Familiar, yes. But efficient? No. They are smoky wood hogs that pump most of their heat up the chimney.

Seeing a working mass heater bench in operation and experiencing its comfortable qualities totally converted me. It is extremely efficient, reaching 90 percent combustion, and almost all heat made is then stored in the cob mass bench, to be slowly released over days!

As for our own bench, it takes about four hours to get totally warm. From a 4-6 hour burn time once a day or every other day, we can maintain a comfortable temperature in the house of about 65°F, even on cold days. The heat from the bench isn't as radiant as a metal stove, but when you get close or sit down on the bench, bring your book and your tea because you will want to stay!

Calleagh: The first real use of the bench was during my labor in late October of 2002. We were birthing at home and we wanted it warm. I ended up using the heated bench as support during our daughter's birth. During her infancy, we slept on a futon on the floor next to it with Shirleen up against the bench because it was cold and frosty (in the 20's) at night. I consider a heated bench an excellent resource for a newborn. I did have to watch it though. More than once while napping on the bench, she got too warm (over time the heat rises through the cushions). I dubbed it the 'overheat-her' bench.

Now, we put all of our clothes under the cushions at night before we go to sleep. The next morning we wake up and start our day with warm clothes! What a luxury in the winter!

—TOM FRAME

Photo: Tom Frame

Three examples of cob buildings that have stood for several centuries in southwest England.

Photo: Catherine Wanek

The fine craftsmanship of Flemming Abrahamsson.
His office, at right, has a gorgeous stove and bench,
pictured below, left. Bottom right: A Rocket Stove powered
staircase, sculpted out of cob. You can just make out the
staircase through the window of the office. Photographs
this page by Catherine Wanek.

Above: The Rocket Mass Heater with bench at lower right in the home of Ianto Evans and Linda Smiley has been in use for over ten years. Dry firewood, split thin and cued up in the sun, small feed barrel and heat exchange barrel nestled in cob.
Below: The continuation of the bench above. Note the thermometer about half-way up on the exposed vertical stack.

Photo: Chris Reinhart

Above: Chris Reinhart's Rocket Stove. Note that the barrel is exposed quite a bit to maximize radiant heat. Below: Kirk Mobert's Rocket Stove with cooking surface on top. There are two cold air intakes below the metal door. The cob bench box keeps firewood dry.

Photo: Kirk Mobert

A ROCKET-FIRED WOOD KILN

In Canada, Jay Naydiuk, who owns a small private lumber mill, built a drying kiln. He used an 8-inch Rocket system with an 8-foot long sand-filled wooden trough for the heat storage and it exhausts to outside the building. A small squirrel-cage fan is moved along the lumber stack at regular intervals to ensure hot air is dispersed equally throughout the pile.

Last year he dried ten thousand board feet (about 25 cubic meters) of his own lumber in batches of about two thousand in a 12 x 20 foot shed about 8 feet high. It took a month with the stove burning about ten hours a day.

Jay's stove has a welded half-inch steel cylindrical burn tunnel and heat riser. To get the extra power of the 40-inch tall heat riser, he added a third of a barrel in height by mounting a 55-gallon drum on top of another one-third of a barrel, which he had cut the bottom out of. It got so hot that the pipe **glowed** orange he says. The kiln temperature ran up to 130°F (though he built the stove at -20°F).

As if its remarkable power output and use isn't enough, it's actually a mobile stove. The whole thing is built in a big pan made out of a 120 gallon oil tank cut in half horizontally so he can drag it out of the building if he needs to. What this means is that his setup is fairly lightweight compared with brick ones with their weighty permanence.

Air supply is from a side vent at burn tunnel level. The feed tube is a capped load chamber sealed with a metal bucket. Jay burns two-foot bolts of his own mill waste that would otherwise be unusable: fir, birch and aspen, but he says larch (tamarack) and lodge pole pine give the best heat. He made his load chamber oversized so even with his 40-inch heat riser the stove doesn't always burn completely clean. The burn tunnel was insulated with wood ash and he felt that its incomplete combustion might have to do with that ash settling and compacting.

He clearly loves his stove, though. He likes the amount of attention it demands. "You have to tickle it," he says. "Rocket Stoves make people feel good. This is a stove for where people abound, where there's community. At one of the first firings of the stove, Trish needed a fireplace poker. I made up an apple crisp and put it on top of the stove on a grate with my big stainless steel mixing bowl over it for an oven. While it was cooking, I forged a poker out of a piece of steel. Then I took the poker and the apple crisp up to Trish's house. That stove makes the best apple crisp I ever tasted."

His application of the Rocket Stove as a lumber dryer is only one of many similar drying applications he feels the system could take on with its gentle heat, from nuts and other edibles to pottery.

He is so enthused by his prototype that he is replacing it with a bigger, ten-inch flue size model. The heat storage will be much more extensive and his plans for the new one include insulating with high temperature mineral wool similar to a fiberglass bat. The horizontal pipe will run the entire length of the building with the pipe doubled back, a total of thirty or forty feet. He intends to put the heat storage into a cob-filled trench in the ground to make his lumber stacks more accessible.

DONKEY'S ROCKET

Kirk Mobert and his family live in a hybrid, natural home-to-be on the California coast in Point Arena. Kirk's story is interesting for a couple of reasons. Not only does his Rocket Stove act as an oven, a stovetop cooker and a heater, he built it without the benefit of this book, having only seen a Rocket Stove during a visit to The North American School of Natural Building. Kirk says, "I invented it as I went along, building from the bottom up. At one point I got hung, the idea is a simple one but it can be hard to visualize fully. So I called Ianto in a panic one night and he gave me the ten minute synopsis. 'The chimneys in the stove, dude.' That was it, everything pretty well clicked after that."

Kirk's stove begins with an oven door made by a metal worker friend. The burn tunnel is massive and can handle several logs burning horizontally. Beyond the burn chamber there is an ash-drop or pit, which burning coals and wood eventually slip into. His fireplace is a horizontal loader with a wide mouth, so the fire can be seen and enjoyed with the front-feed door open. Below the main front door there are two small sliding gates that act as air intake regulators. With the gates open, cool air flows below the length of the burn tunnel, getting a preheat from above before entering flame. The core of the burn chamber is what Kirk calls fireclay cob, "I took fireclay and just made cob with it." The heat riser was cast using refractory cement, poured into the gap between 8-inch and 10-inch cardboard tubes.

From the heat riser top, gases drop down to heat an area where wood waits to dry and a small bench, and finally leaves the system and runs through stovepipe, heating a greenhouse before leaving the building. Weekly maintenance involves "a really long rake-looking thing—a hoe—that fits down the air intake tubes. Occasionaly, ashes pile up and block the airflow, so I shove them back to where they're out of the way, adding to the insulation in the back of the stove." For longer term maintenance there is a clean-out for the stove at the back, on the greenhouse side. A cob plug is wiggled out, ashes are removed and put to use in the greenhouse or straight out the door to the gardens beyond.

Results from Use: The Rocket Kirk made is a wonderful example of taking the principles that make the Rocket Stove work: geometry, proportion and materials, and orienting them to one's own needs. Although now that he has more information, he would do a few things differently, such as try to reduce the temperature of the exit gases. Other nuances of the stove have come with much tinkering; there are spots on the stove which are showing signs of extreme heat stress. The stove is showing cracks and Kirk looks forward to "chopping into it and rebuilding sections again." A work in progress.

THE REINHARTS

Chris and Jennifer Reinhart live in a handmade cob and straw bale cottage in the bumpy part of Indiana, near Bloomington. After their first stove was built, they experienced so many problems with smoke inside their home that they rebuilt it using wisdom gained from their first attempt. Their diligence, imagination and inventiveness have paid off. Here is Chris Reinhart's story in his own words.

Firing off a few of my observations, feelings, and ideas about the Rocket. My back and bottom sides are being warmed by one right now, as I lean against the vertical stack leading up the wall and outside. Jennifer is cozied up over by the barrel and we are both on laptops. I love the feeling of satisfaction that comes from building the device that keeps Jennifer, our son Ethan, and myself warm and cheerful through the winter months. The sound of the Rocket is reassuring: "The heat is on," it says and also tells me when to feed it. Many people who visit the house are more intrigued by the stove than by the walls made of mud and straw, and some have been encouraged to go out and build their own. There's no reason not to, as the materials can be picked up about anywhere. Our Rocket Stove cost less than $100 total and took two weekends to put together; one for the stove, one for the heated bench. When we rebuilt, it took a day to take the stove apart, and a day to put it back together.

This is the second incarnation of the stove and it was built pretty much "by the book."

We had some downdraft problems during the typical stormy fall our first year. Lots of smoke-outs left us feeling rather put out and the first solution we have looked into was the Vacu-Stack (available at chimney

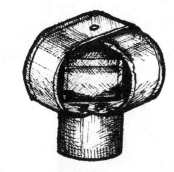

Commercial product: arrangement of baffles creates "suck" as wind blows through.

supplies and online). It is a stovepipe cap that creates suction as high winds blow into it, so it actually draws more in the wind instead of allowing the gases to be blown back into

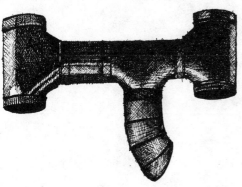

*D.I.Y. Solution: Three T's and a coupler prevent wind from blowing down the flue.
Illustration: Chris Reinhart.*

Illustration: Chris Reinhart

the house. It works great, but to the tune of over $150. This is what we are currently using, with plans to implement the "old-timer's" way of doing things which is three stovepipe T's attached together so that wind blowing in is more likely to keep blowing out rather than turn two corners to go down the pipe into the house. We chose the Vacu-Stack option and saw immediate relief of our problem. With the other changes mentioned in the stove, we have not experienced the problem since then, though it's still too early to tell if it is forever relieved.

When we rebuilt the stove we insulated under and around the tube with perlite contained by brick. Although in planning for the insulation cavities I neglected to plan for an ash pit, which I had built into our first stove. I regret this, because I enjoyed the convenience of an ash pit at the bottom of the burn tunnel. On Jenn's suggestion we began using the shop-vac to clean out the burn tunnel, and it works amazingly well. I always feel that the stove burns best the first few fires after cleaning it.

Perhaps the most significant changes were the added insulation to the feed tube and the change in dimensions. In our first stove, only one side of the horizontal burn tunnel was insulated because it was not planned into the stove.

I changed the dimensions mostly because I used different bricks than in the first stove. In our original stove, we noticed the first and second bricks over the burn tunnel kept breaking and I replaced them three times during our first winter. In our second stove, I replaced the salvaged brick pavers of the burn tunnel that we initially used with fire brick, and thus shifted the dimensions slightly. The entire "J" was 7" x 7" in our first stove and 7" wide by 6" high in the second. The new one gets hotter faster, and the J-tube stays hot for much longer after the fire burns out which makes for effortless start-up for the next fire. I have no quantitative data about the differences between the two, though.

The bench is built of masonry with sand-clay mortar. Urbanite, scrap bricks, sandstone from the creek, and the locally abundant scrap limestone were used mish-mash and built around the flexible stainless steel 8" pipe that a masonry stove-building friend of mine donated.

As for design improvements, partway through building the bench I realized the heat storage capabilities would be improved by building in an open channel between the masonry of the bench and the exterior foundation wall and cob wall. It seems this would slow heat loss to the outside wall and increase the amount of heat going into the mass floor and out into the room.

I like to have the wood split fairly small, 2"–3" in any direction. We have hotter fires with several small pieces rather than a couple of larger ones. Some may consider this excessive splitting a drawback. To me wood splitting is like hitting golf balls or any other focus-oriented physical pursuit. When splitting wood, one knows immediately when one's focus wanes. We burned a cord of wood last year, and that was before the

Chris laying the foundation for the stove. The burn tunnel of brick rests on a bed of perlite. Note Chris is building his first layer of brick and insulation sub-floor level. You can see the completed stove on page 84. Photos, this page, Christopher Reinhart.

building was well sealed around windows, doors and ceiling, and it was a moderately cold year by local standards. I imagine we'll use the same amount or less to heat our 200 round feet this year.

As with any type of fire, it's possible to become hypnotized, and sometimes I find myself squatting in front of the fire box staring into it, with all the crackling and popping of a hot fire and the roar of gases crashing into each other.

—Christopher Reinhart

BERNHARD MASTERSON

Four years ago my partner Le and I decided to embark on a journey toward a greater connection with the natural world: the seasons, gardening, and reducing our need for cash. Since that dream began we have built ourselves a snug 450 square foot hybrid strawbale and cob cottage outside Portland, Oregon. We heat with the sun and a wonderful Rocket Stove.

This is our first winter in the functionally completed house and we are thrilled our dreams are coming true. No longer do we come home in the evening to a cool house and push a button to turn on the furnace, but instead come home to a house that is still comfy and fire up the Rocket Stove. We have a greater awareness of the seasons because we are more involved with actual heating of our house. Every couple of days we get the opportunity to appreciate the weather when we go out to get firewood. I try to take a moment each time to just open my senses and soak in the experience of being outside.

Weekdays we are home in the evenings, and by the time baths are finished the Rocket bench is toasty for bedtime reading. On the weekends we really become cats and look for as many ways as possible to spend time on the bench.

Rocket Stoves are renowned for their efficiency and we surely are pleased with the efficiency of our own. On days with no sun we run our stove two to three hours in the evening, burning about a five gallon bucket full of wood. For regular winter temperatures of 35 to 50°F, this keeps our house at a comfortable 60 to 65°F.

When the weather is windy and colder, 20° to 30°, our house loses about seven degrees a day. This means that in the burn time we have each evening we don't quite make up the heat loss. So in a given 24-hour period we may lose a degree. This doesn't bother us because even by the end of the week our house is still 55° when we get home and 60° when we go to bed, and the bench is always a warm place to hang out. There is also the unexplained feeling that our mud house is warmer than a conventional house at a given temperature. Our weekday burn time is limited because unlike a traditional box stove, we shut down the stove completely and put on the damper before bed. This keeps the heat in our bench from being pushed out of the house by the stored heat in the heat riser.

In designing our stove we chose to keep the top of the barrel low so that we could easily put large pans of water on the top for heating. The three gallons of water we heat on the top of our stove each day we use for dishes and recharging bath water.

Using a 55 gallon drum with a removable clamp-on lid allowed us to build the drum into the wall between the living room and bathroom and still have access to the heat riser for cleaning. The radiant heat in both spaces is wonderful. We have however discovered a couple drawbacks to the clamp-on lid. One is that the bung holes and rings formed in the lid limit the space we have on top of the stove for pans. A second is when we are running the stove really hot the lid expands and pops up slightly which is a little startling when it is covered in pans. Perhaps next year I will try fabricating a new lid from a thicker sheet of steel to solve these imperfections.

I still think the removable lid is a net gain. To seal the bung holes and lid I removed the rubber gaskets and replaced them with

Illustrations: Bernhard Masterson

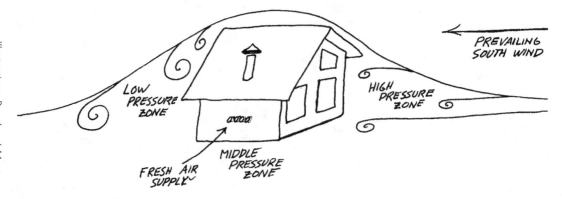

Our other common wind comes fom the north, and pressure zones reverse. The flue still exits in a neutral pressure.

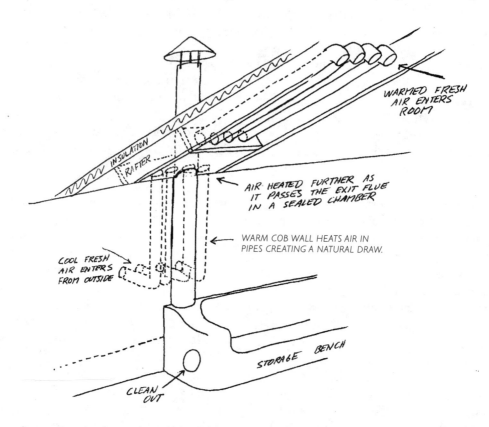

By putting the flue exit and the fresh air supply on the same side of the house, pressure variations between the inside and outside due to wind are balanced. This reduces the load that the J-tube heat pump works against to push combustion gases from the house. The cross-sectional area of the four-inch PVC pipes matches that of our stove's feed tube.

aluminum foil "ropes." This worked well and the aluminum did not degrade at all in the first year of our stove's operation.

Installed in our bench are two six inch diameter ducts for increased surface area for heat transfer to the thermal mass. Our bench is about sixteen feet long. I feel if it was longer we would get more heat out of the exit gases as flue temperatures range from 170 to 250° F as gas exits the house.

The ducts in the bench vary from two to four inches from the surface of the bench, which although not designed that way, turns out to be an asset. We can move around from hotter to cooler parts of the bench depending on our comfort. The two inch spot may be a little on the thin side since it can get quite hot, but it sure reduces the time it takes to proof bread when we set loaves on the bench to rise.

The first stove I built is in a drafty workshop. When we have strong winds hitting the side of the shop where the flue exited it tended to backdraft. I discovered that I could solve this problem by opening up a window on the same side of the shop to balance the pressure in the shop with that on the upwind side. So for our house stove I put a fresh air supply on the same side as the flue to equalize pressure. This has worked well and I built a sort of heat exchanger with the flue to take the chill off the incoming air.

One of my neighbors laughed at our funky stove and the small size of our woodshed as we were building. Now when he comes to visit, his favorite place is on the Rocket bench. And he is envious that we can collect and split our season's supply of fire wood in two days since we heat our house with about a cord of wood. Less wood chopping means more time on the bench, and that is always a good thing.

—BERNHARD MASTERSON

KIKO DENZER

Here are Kiko Denzer's notes about the technical issues of three different rocket mass stoves, followed by a really clever adaptation for a small shop heater based on the principles.

Modular rocket design for a small cabin: I wanted a small, lightweight stove for a 10 x 22 wood cabin; something that would hold more heat than the old cast-iron wood cooking range and that wouldn't create such a risk of chimney fire, or drop bits of coal and hot ash out the holes in the rusted tin that formed the old firebox. I found a heavy metal box 22" square and a 19" maple sugar barrel, then set the box on steel and wood legs off the floor, and built a 6" stove. The very small firebox works very well. I wrapped the bottom third of the barrel, and a short length of flue in cob. The flue exits horizontally through the wall of the box, makes a 180 degree turn back to the stove, and then a 90 degree turn up and out the roof. The chimney was existing, otherwise I'd have thought about sending it out horizontally through a wall. In fact, I might still do that. The exit vent/bench is made of square adobe bricks and stone tiles.

Exit vent/bench made of square adobe bricks and stone tiles: I wasn't coming across much metal tubing, and an odd combination of bench and foundation design didn't leave room for a round tube in places. So I cast adobes and used them to form the vent tunnel under the bench. I had some big slabs of limestone and soapstone, so I used them to span the adobe walls for the seat (also didn't want to risk having the seat crack if someone jumped up there too hard). Mistakes: the adobes were rough, and I didn't smooth plaster them as I built the tunnel (I was thinking extra surface area might improve heat transfer, but the extra drag is noticeable in the stove's operation). I also should have made some thinner adobe "tiles" to give myself more room to make the turns in the bench. As it is, one section of the bench where the turns got too tight had to be bypassed in order to maintain good draft. I had also thought that the top tiles would be easy to remove for clean-out, but they had to be covered with cob to fill gaps, and removal would make too big a mess. Clean-outs in the sidewall of the bench were and are good, however.

Insulative mixes: I've used several different insulative mixes for casting burn tunnels, including refractory cement (expensive) and pumice, as well as a clay-sawdust mix fortified with Portland cement (cheaper, but also softer). It seems that any lightweight aggregate makes a very soft material that degrades much faster than hard firebrick so it's not an experiment I've pursued further. The sawdust clay mix however (without any added Portland) made a fine insulator for the riser—all the sawdust burnt out, leaving a very lightweight clay foam. The foam is very fragile, but held up fine until I rebuilt the stove. When I touched it, it collapsed. If need be, it could perhaps be made stronger by using purer clay (fireclay?) and perhaps thicker slip.

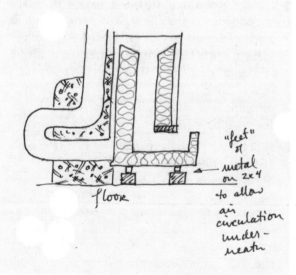

Another example of adaptations based on Rocket Stove principles: I just made a little Rocket radiator for my shop/studio: Basic design is the same, but instead of directing the flow of hot gases through the narrow

gap between exchange barrel and insulated heat riser, I just extended the chimney in three long sections connected by 180 degree turns—a big radiator to provide heat fast with a small amount of fuel. The firebox is the same cross sectional area as the 6" system, but adjustable so I can burn a very few very small sticks, quite slowly, and have the heat from them instantly, which is more of what I need in the shop environment. Also good for cleaning up scraps from wood projects.

—Kiko Denzer

FLEMMING ABRAHAMSSON

Flemming Abrahamsson is an ecological architect, building contractor, master mason and master thatcher. He is famous in Scandinavia for his brilliant ecological designs. See pages 82 and 56 for examples of Flemming's work.

We had the pleasure in 1997 to have the first cob building workshop in Denmark.

At the workshop there were many skilled craftsmen and other masons who in their daily work built masonry stoves. The meeting between Ianto and the other pyromaniacs immediately inspired a whole lot of experiments with fireplaces and ovens.

None of us who live so far north with a cold winter have ever forgotten this session.

From this workshop the ideas about cob, baking ovens, bench stoves, and Rockets spread like a fire to all of Denmark.

The first bench stove in Denmark was built in cob with an oil drum as heat riser with a 5-meter long exhaust pipe in the bench. The exhaust pipe dives into the clay floor after it travels through the bench. Then after another 2 meters, it comes up in the middle of the house in an 8-inch round flue. Ianto and I measured 1000°C (1800°F) in the combustion chamber and 32°C (90°F) in the top of the chimney—the rest of the heat was kept inside the house.

Another project we did was for the public schools in Copenhagen. They have a common place where they train the school children in physics and chemistry. Here they demonstrate industrial production of energy such as coal, electricity and natural gas.

The children decided very quickly that they should also demonstrate how firewood is used for energy. So we built a Rocket bench stove and a baking oven. From these stoves, the hot gases, instead of being lost up the chimney, will be used to heat a hot air balloon.

In another classroom we built a 3½ ton Rocket masonry stove, which heats the room and a water-heating radiator—so that the children understand where the heat comes from.

—FLEMMING ABRAHAMSSON

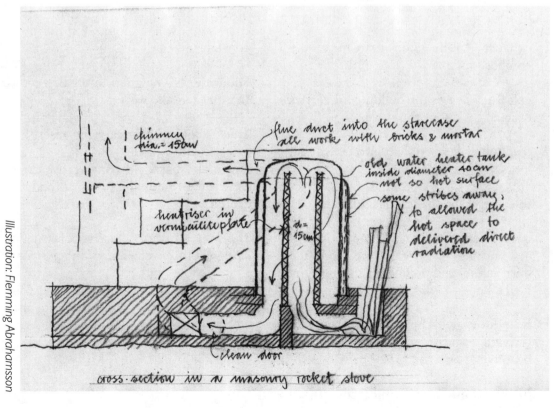

Illustration: Flemming Abrahamsson

Glossary

Here you'll find our definitions of some of the terms found in this book.

burn tunnel – horizontal duct connecting feed tube to heat riser.

cob – mineral-fiber composite building material made of clay soil, sand, water and straw, smeared together damp to cohesive consistency.

combustion unit – all parts of a Rocket Stove that enclose fire.

cord – unit of firewood measurement, a stack of four feet wide, four feet high by eight feet long.

duct – pipe, any shape, that carries gas or air.

exhaust – all ducts downstream of the combustion unit.

exit flue – leaves the building, or carries exhaust gas out of the stove.

feed tube – vertical shaft into which fuel feeds itself by gravity.

flue – any duct that carries hot gases.

heat riser – internal chimney carrying burning/burnt gases up from the burn tunnel and pulling air through the feed tube.

heat storage – heavy masonry mass through which exhaust gases pass, heating it.

hydrocarbon – any chemical comprising only hydrogen and carbon.

hypocaust – under-floor heating system of ducts carrying hot gases.

Lorena stove – cookstove system using a sand-clay block which is excavated to accommodate fire and cook pots.

kindling – thin, easily ignited wood used to get a fire going quickly.

pyrolysis – chemical decomposition of fuel by heat but without oxygen.

Rumford fireplace – high efficiency open fireplace built to a fixed geometry.

specific heat – the amount of heat a material will store, proportional to water.

squatments – neighborhoods that evolve by squatter takeovers.

stack – vertical duct carrying gases.

thermal mass – comparative term describing total ability of a body to store heat.

thermal battery – heavy construction designed to store heat for long periods.

Urbanite – broken up concrete slabs, e.g. from driveways, sidewalks, etc. used in construction.

More Information

RESOURCES ON PYROMANIA

Cob Cottage Company. Take Pyromania workshops, find updates to this publication, access the brain trust of Ianto Evans on Rocket Stoves and other things related to Natural Building and find the very best Natural Building books available at the mail order bookstore:

Box 942
Coquille, OR 97423
Phone: (541) 942-2005
Website: www.cobcottage.com

For technical advice and anecdotal commiseration, or to tell us about the stove you've built, contact us:
Ianto through Cob Cottage, above.
Leslie: www.rocketstoves.com

We have on hand a list of fellow pyros who have built these stoves and take great pleasure in thinking and talking about fire. They can perhaps answer some of your questions or come to your site to give advice. Some will charge a fee, some will not. Perhaps you'd like a workshop at your site, or for your group or school, etc. Contact us for referrals.

Leslie Jackson teaches workshops in Pocket Rockets to schools, natural building groups, sustainability fairs, etc. Traveling with all of the materials to build a Pocket Rocket, and leaving a few Rockets behind, her demonstrations get people thinking about fire and efficient wood burning.

You may order copies of this book, download the digital version, find local Rocket Stove builders, workshops, further case studies and many detailed photographs of the insides and outsides of Rocket Stoves at:
www.rocketstoves.com

BOOKS ON NATURAL BUILDING AND WOOD BURNING

★Evans, Ianto, Linda Smiley and Michael G. Smith. *The Hand-Sculpted House: A Practical And Philosophical Guide To Building A Cob Cottage.* Chelsea Green Publishing Co. 2002.

★Smith, Michael G. *The Cobber's Companion: How to Build Your Own Earthen Home.* A Cob Cottage Publication. 1997.

★Kennedy, Joseph, Michael G. Smith and Catherine Wanek, Editors. *The Art of Natural Building.* New Society Publishing Co. 2002.

*Evans, Ianto. *Lorena Owner-Built Stoves.* Volunteers in Asia. 1980. (reprint).

Soderstrom, Neil. *Heating Your Home with Wood.* Harper and Row. 1978.

Shelton, Jay. *The Woodburner's Encyclopedia.* Vermont Crossroads Press. 1976, etc.

Barden, Albert and Heikki Hyytiainen. *Finnish Heating Stoves: Heart of the Home.* 1988.

★Denzer, Kiko. *Build Your Own Earth Oven: A Low-Cost, Wood-Fired Mud Oven; Simple Sourdough Bread; Perfect Loaves.* Hand-Print Press. 2000-2007.

Lyle, David. *The Book of Masonry Stoves.* Chelsea Green Publishing Co. 2000.

Orton, Vrest. *The Forgotten Art of Building a Good Fireplace: The Story of Sir Benjamin Thompson, Count Rumford, an American Genius.* Yankee, Inc. 1969.

★Chiras, Dan and Cedar Rose Guelberth. *The Natural Plaster Book: Earth, Lime and Gypsum Plasters for Natural Homes.* New Society Publishers. 2002.

★Denzer, Kiko. *Dig Your Hands in the Dirt! A Manual for Making Art out of Earth.* Hand-Print Press. 2005.

★Ludwig, Art. *Principles of Ecological Design.* Oasis Design. 2003.

*Ludwig, Art. *Create an Oasis with Greywater. Your Complete Guide to Choosing, Building, and Using Grey Water Systems.* Oasis Design. 1994-2006.

*Ludwig, Art. *Builders Greywater Guide. Installation of Greywater Systems in New Construction and Remodeling.* Oasis Design. 1995-2004.

*Ludwig, Art. *Water Storage: Tanks, Cisterns, Aquifers, and Ponds.* Oasis Design. 2005.

*Kahn, Lloyd. *Home Work: Handbuilt Shelter.* Shelter Publications. 2004.

*Kahn, Lloyd and Bob Easton. *Shelter.* Shelter Publications. Second Edition. 2000.

★*Available by mail from Cob Cottage.*

ABOUT COB COTTAGE CO.

Our inspiration comes from direct observation of Nature and from the wisdom of traditional cultures. We are committed to deconsumerizing, to reducing the flow of cash resources and waste, and helping others to do the same. We work with a wide range of natural materials.

We conduct hands-on research on natural building methods and materials, testing our own buildings by living in them.

Cob Cottage Company runs the North American School of Natural Building, the first permanent teaching center for Natural Builders in the US.

Through **practical trainings** in natural construction, we help empower ordinary people to build their own houses at moderate cost. See our website at cobcottage.com for a current workshop list.

By mail and phone, and through publications and tours, we supply information, support and inspiration for people to make healthy choices about buildings.

Our **"Pyromania!" workshops** are for those in love with fire. Learn how fire burns, what makes combustion efficient, how to build the ultimate in snug, energy-saving campfires, stoves, and fireplaces for cooking and comfort, all hand-made at almost no cost. We burn and evaluate several models, as well as build one or two. Cob Cottage Company is the only group offering such workshops (that we know of) and they often occur spontaneously and fill up quickly. Keep an eye on the Schedule of Workshops in the Cob Cottage Company website (at cobcottage.com) and let us know if you'd like to be placed on a Pyromania alert list.

Dozens of cob demonstration buildings all over North America are now open to visitors.

Ianto Evans is an applied ecologist, landscape architect, inventor, writer and teacher, with building experience on six continents. He teaches ecological building and has consulted to USAID, World Bank, US Peace Corps and several foreign governments on improved cook stoves, fuel supplies and kitchen technology. Ianto developed the Lorena stove in the 1970's in Guatemala—the first really successful widespread self-help cook stove. He has thirty years experience with research promoting and building woodfired stoves. He was a founder of Aprovecho Institute, Cob Cottage Company and the North American School of Natural Building.

Leslie Jackson is a natural builder, an educator and a musician. She is an independent publisher, helping writers by playing several roles (from collaborator to editor and from coordinator to layout designer) in order to see a book evolve from the dream to the shelf. Between book projects, she gives workshops in Rocket Stoves and natural building subjects and consults for the local natural building community. Leslie lives at the juncture between high and low tech in Oakland, Ca.

AFTERWORD

In late Fall, 2005, Ianto gathered three of us together to prepare for this edition: Two hand-picked pyromaniacs, Kirk "Donkey" Mobert, Ernie Wisner and myself. For two weeks, Kirk and Ernie tinkered, built, broke, brainstormed Rocket Stoves and drank copious amounts of coffee that was brewed on obscure woodburning inventions that Ianto has been collecting. I asked questions and wrote and drew. We were occasionally interrupted by pin-point questions from Ianto, who mostly puttered in his vegetable garden. It was much like the Pyromania! workshops at Cob Cottage in its spirit of play and inquisition, but it was more like a retreat in its absolute immersion. We ate, drank, talked, dreamt and breathed fire. At the end of the time, we were left with more questions than we sought to answer and we were left with the conclusion that the key to a good stove is to test *a lot* to get the results you want. Also, this stove isn't just for pyros and scientists. With an understanding of the principles, shapes and materials anyone can build a good Rocket Stove and take charge of their heat and comfort.—Leslie Jackson

THANKS

We're only certain of a few things in life. Apart from the inevitability of death (taxes are somewhat optional), we're sure of one fact: we will have forgotten to mention some people who helped a lot. Sorry. If you let us know, you'll go in the next edition.

So, in no special order:
Linda Smiley
Bart Trickel
Kiko Denzer
Bernhard Masterson
Flemming Abrahamsson
Bjarne Wickstrom
Pat Loomis
Michael G. Smith
Tim Kring
Robert L. Arson
Susan Kleihauer
Hop Kleihauer
Tom Frame
Calleagh Ferrara
Art Ludwig
Shannon Dealy
Larry Jacobs
Elke Cole
Coenraad Rogmans
Larry Winiarski
Dennis Kuklok
Nelson Flystrap
Meka
Kirk "Donkey" Mobert
Ernie Wisner
Chris Reinhart
Jack Stephens
Jay Naydiuk

Cob Cottage Publications,
2004, 2005, 2006, 2007

Cover credits

Front cover:
Photo: Bernhard Masterson
Lettering: Ianto Evans

Back cover:
Photo, top: Kirk "Donkey" Mobert
Photo, bottom: Mark Kohlhaas

Pixel farming: Kirk "Donkey" Mobert